SHAMAI

Milarepa - from Anger to Enlightenment

- A biographical novel -

by HÜMÜH
Clear-Mind Buddhist
Maticintin
Wisdom Master

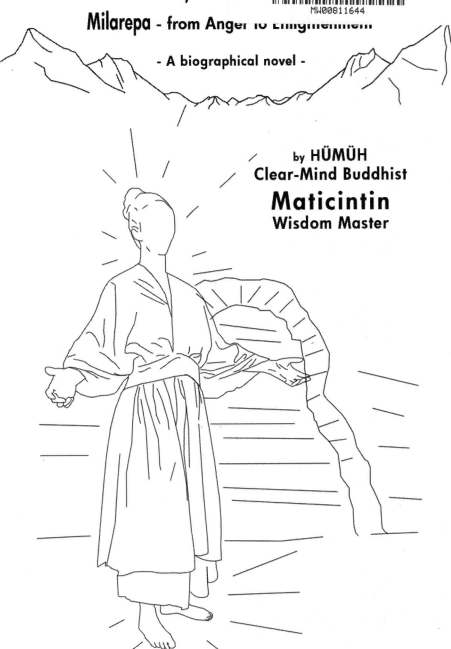

Dharmavidya Publishing

Shaman of Tibet

International Copyright © 2020 Maticintin
Printed in the United States of America
Dharmavidya Publishing

Seventh Printing: 2020
Sixth Printing: 2008
Fifth Printing: 2003
Fourth Printing: 2000
Third Printing: 1996
Second Printing: 1994
Originally Published: The Golden Dream 1987

Library of Congress Calalog No.: 87-70596
ISBN: 978-0-932927-10-1

Cover Design: Monika Mueller
Illustrations: Henry Calero

DHARMAVIDYA PUBLISHING
◆

1-6055 Kettle River FSR East, Westbridge, BC V0H 1Y0 Canada
607 E. Beale St., Kingman, AZ 86401 U.S.A.
P.O. Box 2700, Oroville, WA 98844 U.S.A.
Phone/Fax (250) 446-2022 / Phone Orders (800) 336-6015
E-mail: DharmavidyaPublishing@HUMUH.org

What is a Shaman?

A shaman, in the truest sense, is an aspect of the Transhistorical Consciousness, which means that one is divinity personified with a role in life. This role is, first, personal refinement, and after that foundation has been laid, that refinement lives without expectation of reward in service to all life. So, contrary to public opinion, a shaman is not characterized by drums, rattles and incantations, but rather, by a definitive consciousness that is divine, or one with all life. This is the definition of a shaman in its purest form.

Maticintin
Wisdom Master

Wisdom Master Maticintin is a vessel of the Mind Treasure Teachings, gifted her by the Transhistorical Consciousness, meaning she attained enlightenment in another lifetime. Maticintin gained enlightenment, benefits from the great Wisdom Master Padmasambhva. In the Buddhist Scriptures, Maticintin is referred to as Sugata Maticintin, the 991st Historical Buddha.

The Wisdom Master has a Doctorate in Logic and Buddhism and is the Founder and Leader of HÜMÜH: Jeweled Path of Living Wisdom, Clear-Mind Buddhism. The Wisdom Master currently teaches at a variety of HÜMÜH Meditation Centers in the United States and Canada, including the HÜMÜH Dharma/Meditation Center in Kingman, Arizona, and the Skycliffe HÜMÜH Monastery in Westbridge, British Columbia. She also travels and teaches at other locations in the United States, Canada, and occasionally, abroad.

Maticintin is a noted author with many books, among them a fresh, poetic rendering of *The Heart Sutra*; the illuminating *Clear-Light Living Meditation, Vol. 1, Secrets of the Golden Spiral*, which is HÜMÜH's *Handbook for Enlightenment*, as well as *Chod: Cutting Through Obstacles*. She brought forth HÜMÜH as a new Buddhist sect in 1992 as an expression of the highest Teachings culled from all Buddhism to directly address the Western body/mind/spirit connection and lifestyle.

One of the manifestations of her dedication as a Spiritual Teacher is the Initiate Home-Study Program she has developed, which enables Initiates to work with her at a distance, as well as, through on-site retreats and classes. While keeping up with a year-round Teaching schedule, the Wisdom Master maintains periods of solitude in between working with her students and takes time to hike in nature and be in companion energy with a romping, sable-haired Victorian Pomeranian named Tantra, which refers to the rapid *means* to enlightenment.

*Dedicated to every person
who desires spiritual heights
but fears they can never
really make it.*

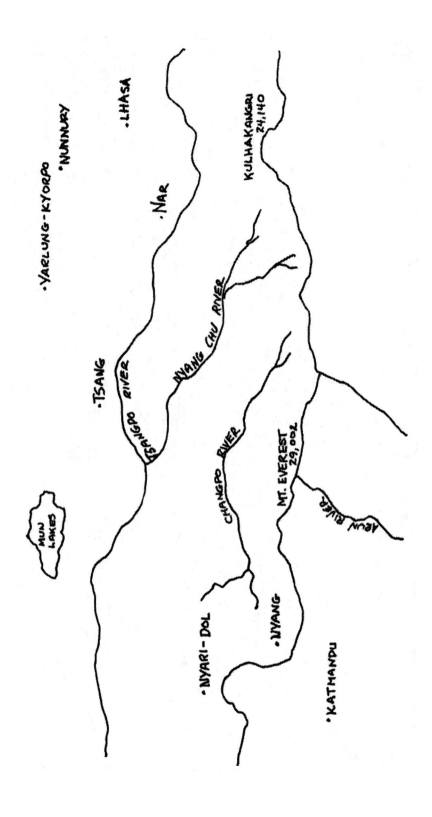

SHAMAN OF TIBET

TABLE OF CONTENTS

PRELUDE
HUMHUMHUMHUMHUMHUMHUM**HUMUH**

Rechung gazed into the faces of those seated about him. They were the faces of the Jetsun's disciples and of those devotees who had heard in the nearby cities that Milarepa was near death. Many believed him already to be dead. He wondered what he could say to put them at ease, but his heart too was heavy and he could think of nothing.

"Does the Jetsun live?" one woman called out from the crowd.

"Yes," another called. "Did we really see the Guru fly or was it his spirit?"

One man rose to his feet, raising himself to eye level with Rechung, who was seated on a rock platform inside of the Jetsun's cave. "I was outside my home in the village," the man began, "when, for no apparent reason, my eyes were drawn upward. There, seated in lotus position, was the Jetsun Milarepa, gliding gracefully across the sky."

A woman jumped to her feet and called out, "When I saw the Guru, he was flying through the air like a bird, his arms outstretched from his sides."

Another woman stood quickly and said that she too had seen Milarepa flying but that he was lying on his back, staring up into the heavens, when she had seen him. Then, suddenly, nearly everyone, except the Guru's closest disciples, was standing, talking in union about what each had seen.

Rechung raised himself to a kneeling position and extended his hands for silence. Gradually, those standing seated themselves again. Rechung hesitated, slowly drawing in a deep breath in an effort to gain time to choose his words. At last, in a strong voice, he spoke to the people. "Jetsun Milarepa has given each of you a sign because of your devotion to him. You have come because, in some special way, each of you has earned the right to be here. Be patient! You are here for a reason. The Vi-Guru wishes to speak with you." He paused, looking out at the intense faces of those gathered. "Please, be patient," he said again.

A soft murmur went through the crowd. The people had heard that the Guru had been poisoned and was lying on the very edge of death, and many believed that, having seen Milarepa flying through the sky, they had witnessed a sign that the great one had already died.

"The Vi-Guru lives!" Rechung called out in a reassuring voice. "He is not here himself at this moment because he asked for a time to regain his strength. He will speak with you later, as he has said he would."

"Is it true that he has been poisoned?" a man in the back row called out.

Rechung lowered his head a moment and then raised it again. "Yes. Yes, it is true," he said sorrowfully.

"But he still lives?" the man asked again.

"He still lives," Rechung answered reassuringly. A knot formed in the back of his throat, making it difficult for him to speak. He was not sure he could bear the Guru's passing.

"Who did it?" a woman in the front row yelled. "Who dared to murder the saint Milarepa?"

Rechung hesitated, slowly choosing his words. "One who believed that the poison would test his authenticity arranged to give poisoned food to the Jetsun. It was a priest who paid another to give him the poison. The priest believed that a true saint would know of the poison and not eat the food or, at least, not suffer ill effects from it."

A murmur went through the gathering of people again. They were discussing the deed of the priest and why Milarepa had eaten the food. Rechung waited until they quieted and then continued. "That very morning, Milarepa told his disciples that he would be poisoned that day," Rechung said uneasily.

"Then why didn't you stop him?" someone called out.

"Yes," another yelled, "if you knew that he would be given poison, why didn't you test the food before he ate it?"

Rechung shifted his weight uneasily. "It is the way of the Vi-Guru," he said sadly. "I cannot tell you more. I am as filled with sorrow as you are. For days, I have been questioning how it could have happened and why it did not happen to me instead. I would gladly give up my life to save Milarepa."

"And so would I," a woman wailed.

A man in the back row jumped to his feet. "And I, as well!" he called out.

Still another and another rose to their feet, offering their lives in exchange for Milarepa's, until finally all those gathered were standing. Tears and sobs of anguish filled the air and Rechung and the other disciples lowered their heads, weeping with them.

Suddenly, a hush fell over them. Without a word, everyone sat down. Their eyes were raised to a golden light in which a thin and frail, bald, round-faced man, wearing a maroon robe and carrying a short walking stick, was seating himself next to Rechung. It was the Jetsun Milarepa, the Vi-Guru. He gracefully raised one hand in blessing. His eyes were dark, twinkling buttons and his expression serene. A scent of roses filled the room and, because there was not a movement or even the sound of anyone's breath, the faint, haunting hum of a conch shell could be heard blowing in the distance. Rechung made an effort to slip back, behind the Guru, but Milarepa motioned with his hand that he was to stay.

"Rechung has agreed to tell you my story," Milarepa said, pausing. His eyes shone and his lips curled into a slight smile. "The story he will tell is one he has recorded for me. I asked him to write it down, so that all who believe themselves unworthy of seeking enlightenment will know that being worthy is merely a condition of mind." He paused, looking out over the faces of those seated before him and then continued. "It is not the pious who inherit the higher consciousness, but rather, higher consciousness is earned by those who dare to strive for it. You will understand when you hear the story of my youth. Listen to it closely. Give Rechung your full attention. When he has finished, you will know why it is time for me to leave you." Milarepa turned and looked at Rechung. He smiled lovingly at him. "Tell them, my son. Tell them of my early life, as I told it to you."

Rechung gazed lovingly at Milarepa in return and then turned to face those gathered before him. He reached for the tablets on which he had recorded the Jetsun's story and slowly began to read aloud. It was as though the Vi-Guru himself was telling the story. After a moment, he hesitated, turning to Milarepa who nodded his approval and then closed his eyes.

Rechung's telling of Milarepa's story:

Listen with your heart.

PART ONE
BONDAGE

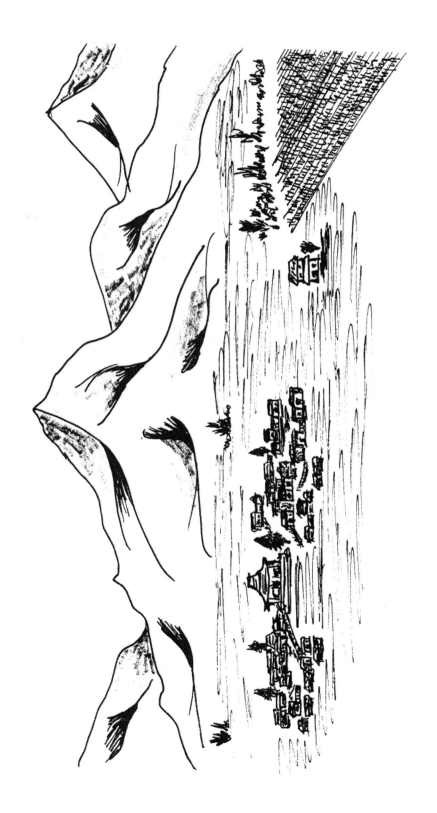

CHAPTER ONE

A CHANGE IN DESTINY

"**M**ila, you're not listening to me," Zesay said, turning on her heels and pouring me a cup of the thick butter-salt tea. "We could be married and move away from here. No one would know us in Katmandu. Our life would be a clean slate. My parents would give us their blessings." She hesitated, standing over me as I sat, with my head lowered, on floor cushions next to the stove. How could I tell her that such an idea was out of the question. I knew that Zesay was afraid and so was I. We had been promised to each other from birth and yet my mother could delay fulfillment of that promise for an endless time. "We are of marrying age," she said sadly.

I looked up at her, watching as she poured her own tea and sat down opposite me. Her eyes were filled with tears and, looking into them, I could feel the pain my silence was causing her and yet I dared not speak. Instead, I remembered with slight bitterness how sweet our early childhood had been, how we played and dreamed about our future together. But then things changed.

My father, Mila-Dorje-Senge, died. Although he left all of his vast wealth, the greatest in all the valley, to me, my mother, and my sister, on his deathbed he gave charge of that wealth to my paternal aunt and uncle, who were to guard and administer it until I was old enough to assume position as head of the family. My father's brother and his wife were to care for our family and to comfort us; but instead, they took possession of the property, including the main house, claiming the fortune as their own and bound my family to servitude. My mother, once the matriarch of the whole valley, became a penniless laborer, working in the fields that were once her own to earn a meager living for herself and her two children. Only the relatives on her side of the family and Zesay's family remained comforters. The other families in the valley, although sympathetic, were in the employ of my wicked aunt and uncle and offered no assistance for fear of losing their jobs.

I looked at Zesay, who was sitting across from me. Signs of womanhood swelled on her chest. Her neck was long and slender, supporting a jutting chin, which proudly tilted upward. The tears in her eyes had dried and her expression was now determined rather than sad.

"It will not help for you to avenge your mother," Zesay said firmly. "The Lama Kataka has said that one must be detached from negative feelings to find happiness."

I studied the firm set of my beloved's jaw. She was proud, but naturally so, and there was a sense of inner strength about her that enhanced her attractiveness. While I loved her, I also admired her. Few had the nerve to sit at the Lama Kataka's feet and listen with an open heart. My own mother was terrified of the man. She claimed he had a glint in his eyes that was unnaturally pure and that if it were to rub off on us, we would grow complacent in our state of poverty and be destined to live in it forever. It made her uneasy that Zesay visited him and she made me promise that I would never go with Zesay to the old man's hovel. I didn't go but I enjoyed hearing Zesay tell of ideas she had gathered from him. Often we would sit for hours, talking about what she had learned. Sometimes I would ask questions, challenging her just to move deeper into a subject. Zesay was always patient, explaining the Lama's teaching as best she could. At times she even asked the Lama a question for me. Some of the answers were easy to understand and others didn't make sense to me, like how I could be detached from the feelings my mother had stirred in me. It was impossible.

I stared at Zesay, knowing full well that neither she nor the Lama had any idea what it was like to have a mother like mine. There was no doubt in my mother's mind that it was my responsibility to avenge my family. I had heard it many times since my father's death, and each time my mother's hatred for my aunt and uncle was greater than the time before. Perhaps if I had shown more hatred myself, my mother's would have lessened. But it wasn't my nature to hate. Instead, all my life I had tried to ignore it, to put my attention on what life could offer, rather than what it did not offer.

I recalled how I had been at a peasant feast in the lower village of Tsa. Even though I was penniless, the peasants knew that I was of noble birth and offered me the head of the table, honoring me. Without a doubt I had enjoyed myself. Kegs of freshly brewed chang beer were tapped, and the cool, thick liquid soothed the tensions of my home life. I sat with them, drinking until late in the day, then stumbled home. My mother found me singing without a care on the road to our house. "With all our problems, my son has become a useless drunkard!" she screeched. Then she bent to the ground, grabbed up a stick, and began to beat me with it, yelling, "It is time for you to take steps to reclaim our family fortune." She demanded that I journey to the provinces of U and Tsang, where it was reputed that a great sorcerer lived, to beg to be taken in as an apprentice. The purpose of the apprenticeship was to gain the power to punish my wicked aunt and uncle for stealing our home, land, and possessions and to right the wrong that had been done to my family. Worst of all, my mother now threatened that if I did not succeed, she would kill herself. I would be cursed for life.

I sipped my tea, remembering the bitterness of my mother's tongue. I had no other choice but to leave.

Zesay raised her hand to mine, touching me lightly.

I looked at her, suddenly caught by her unusual beauty and the knowledge that she belonged to me, had always belonged to me, as promised by our parents at her birth. We could belong to no other and yet an uncertain feeling told me that I was not to have her at all. I couldn't bear the thought of it. As my eyes caressed her slender neck and rose to her lips, my new manhood awakened.

"We can be married," Zesay said, wrapping her small fingers around my large hand. She was aware of my sudden rise in feeling.

"We can go to the sorcerer together."

I was struck by her offer. "You would do that for me? You would go against the teaching of the Lama Kataka and all that you believe and love?"

"I love you," she said, steadily gazing at me.

"And you would, in turn, do evil for your love of me?" I asked again.

Zesay lowered her eyes. "Is that not what you intend doing for your mother?" she asked, pausing to look up at me again. "I would not be turning to evil," she said, "I would be with you."

"But I am to turn to evil, Zesay! My mother has cursed me with the responsibility of destroying those who have destroyed her. You told me yourself that the Lama Kataka said that when one joins another in a deed, one takes on the other's karma. In this case you would be taking on my evil karma." I hesitated, studying the downward tilt of her head. I knew she was listening carefully. "I am to have a change in destiny," I said, "and you must not join me in it."

Zesay looked up at me quickly. There was a sharpness to her gaze. "Your mother is not destroyed by your aunt and uncle. They have merely taken her possessions. She destroys herself with her anger."

I stared at my beloved. It was not the first time I had heard such ideas from her. I knew they were the ideas of the Lama Kataka. "My mother will kill herself if I do not succeed," I answered finally.

"She will destroy herself if you do succeed, as well," Zesay answered. "Can't you see that her hatred has doomed her already?"

I shook my head. "It is not for me to say that she is doomed or not doomed, or whether she dooms herself or has been doomed by another. It is not my position to be the judge. It is my position to carry out my mother's wishes."

Zesay drew in a long, deep breath and let it out slowly, as if she knew that it was no use arguing the social order of the family and a young man's responsibility within it. Still, she could not help but try. "We could be married. I would wait for you here. At least the difficulties you face would not seem so great after we have shared the pleasure of our togetherness." She hesitated.

I stared at Zesay. A desperate rise in feeling rushed through me. She wanted me as her husband and she was afraid that if we did not marry now, we would never marry. Desire to draw her next to me, to thrust my throbbing penis into her, was almost beyond control. I reached between my legs to calm myself but that part of me had swollen to great proportions. I knew that once I tasted pleasure with her, I would be driven by the memory of it. I first had to fulfill my responsibility to my mother. Quickly I sprang to my feet, my body quivering in the wake of my desires. I stood over Zesay, unable to explain myself and yet certain that she knew. "I will return when the deed is done," I said in an unsteady voice. Then I turned and ran through the doorway, running in hopes that the motion would relieve the tension built up between my legs.

Nyangtsha Kargyen, my mother, turned and stared at me. She looked at me, aware that I was still merely a boy. She reminded me that even though I was fifteen, my years had been hard ones, leaving me with the appearance of one nearing twenty. She continued to explain that I would have looked older still, but my boyish grin and plump flesh hid the sad, faraway look in my eyes.

Gazing at her in the long silence that followed, I sensed that she did not really want me to go. I also knew that she was concerned that, without direction and purpose, I would become a drunkard. Many times she had told me that the villagers encouraged my drinking because they pitied me. "Your life with the clan and with Zesay will have to wait," she had said. "You will have no life, no real life, until you avenge me and your sister and have laid claim to your father's last will and testament."

"You will leave today," Nyangtsha Kargyen said to me. Then she handed me the new robe she had sewn for me and a shoulder pack of barley, oats, and dried meat. "In the pocket of the robe are two gold coins. I have no more to give you." She paused, studying me. I thought she was going to say more about the money when she said, "Follow the road to Tsang and do not dally. On the other side of the city you will come to the village Yarlung-Kyorpo. Ask there for the great black magician. His name is Lama Yungtun-Trogyal. Give him your gold coins and beg him to teach you the secrets of revenge. Learn how to make a hailstorm to destroy your evil aunt and uncle's crops and whatever it takes to eliminate their lineage and to make them bend to your demands." She paused, gazing at me. "I will spin my prayer wheels for you every hour until, in my heart, I am sure you are there."

I looked at my mother, knowing that there was nothing I could say to soften her, yet I knew that, in her way, she truly loved me. Although she was filled with hatred and anger, she would continue to pray for my safety, even if I did not reach my destination for many months. She would know, somehow, if I arrived or not. I then dared to speak of my greatest concern. "Suppose I do not find the black magician," I said, "or suppose he refuses to teach me the black arts."

Nyangtsha Kargyen looked at me for a long time without answering. I knew that she would not allow me to fail in my mission, that my failure would destroy what little quality of life we shared as a family. "You must persuade him," she said finally. "You must persuade him at all costs, even if it means your death." She hesitated, allowing the full impact of her words to strike me. "You must return with full powers of the black arts to avenge our name. You must return and destroy your aunt and uncle." She paused again, this time seemingly out of breath, looking deeply into me. I recognized the look. It was the one that said, "You look so much like your dead father." "If you fail, I will kill myself," she said firmly.

A cold chill rushed through me. I searched my mother's face for tenderness and comfort but there was none. Her eyes were cold stones. As wife of my father she had been known as the White Jewel of Nyang. Now, where once there had been gaiety in her face, there was somberness. Her features were old and tired, and she spoke, not of feasting and joy, but of killing and revenge. She had become an angry old woman. Yet I knew that she still loved me. "I will succeed," I said. I was uneasy and self-conscious when I turned to my sister Peta, who was standing to the left of Nyangtsha Kargyen in front of the cooking pots. She was wringing her hands in an effort to keep from sobbing aloud. Tears streamed down her cheeks. I wanted to rush to her and comfort her but my mother's presence separated us. "Oh, I'll be all right," I called out to her, trying not to appear frightened. "It's not as if I have to become a holy man like Lama Kataka. If I did, I would really be in trouble." I laughed lightly to encourage her.

Peta let out a short laugh and then began to cry again.

I bowed before my mother.

Nyangtsha Kargyen stood unyieldingly before me. "Learn to make hailstorms and return home to destroy your aunt and uncle's crops," she said again, pausing long enough to make sure the lightness had left me and that I was listening. "Learn to kill with black magic, Mila, and return to extinguish the descendants of those who have done us harm." She paused, reached into her gown pocket and withdrew a cloth, unfolding it to reveal a map, then refolded it and handed it to me. "You must claim your birthright and establish myself and your sister Peta in our rightful positions. I told you that if you fail, I will kill myself. It is true. I will do it." She paused again, the corners of her mouth relaxed in a downward position. She appeared to be both sad and angry. "If you fail," she repeated weakly, "I will kill myself."

I lowered my eyes, unable to look at my mother any longer. My heart was heavy. I quickly cast a glance at Peta and then turned. My feet felt heavy and difficult to lift, but I forced myself to leave, hurrying through the door.

CHAPTER TWO

THE ROAD TO TSANG

The road to Tsang was narrow, and each time a yak cart came toward me, I jumped into the ditch at the side of the road and waited for it to pass. I wished the carts were going in the opposite direction so that I could beg a ride, but that was not the case.

On one occasion, I slipped on a moist embankment. I quickly put out my hand to stop the fall and save myself from the mud below. Although I avoided the rancid slush, I sharply twisted my wrist and, for a moment, thought it had been broken. I stood in pain, unmoving, clasping my wrist with my other hand. The cart driver saw what had happened and stopped.

"You all right?" the peasant farmer called, tightly holding the reins of his yak, which shifted restlessly after the sudden stop.

I looked up at him and nodded, opening and closing the fingers of my left hand, testing them. Then, with the other hand, I lifted the palm up and down to make sure that the joint was movable.

"The road is too narrow," the peasant farmer said. "It should be widened."

I nodded again, still recovering from the pain. My depression seemed to mask it somewhat.

"Where you headed?" the peasant farmer called.

"Tsang," I answered in a numb voice. I looked up into the driver's face. I felt as if I had met the man before but I didn't care to ask, wanting to be left alone.

"Tsang is three weeks' journey from here," the driver said, eyeing me curiously. "You ever been there before?"

I wished that the driver would move on and permit me to climb from the ditch. "It will soon be three weeks and one day," I answered smartly.

The peasant narrowed his eyes and studied me. I felt him staring at my clothes. I was wearing a new robe that was tied at the waist by a finely woven rope. I looked, I knew, like a mixture of nobleman and farm hand. My hair was swept back into a neat knot. "Ever been to Tsu?" the driver asked.

I looked squarely at the driver, about to tell him to get out of my way, but there was something about the man's eyes that made me hold my tongue. He was a large man with a face that was rugged and square, his chest was thick from working the plow, and his arms were massive. I suddenly recognized him. "At the feast last week," I answered.

"You're the young nobleman who sat at the head of the table," the peasant said, smiling.

I bowed, unable to shake my uneasiness. I remembered how I had been drawn to the man and how others had admired him. He had watched over me at the feast. It was he who had me placed at the head of the table. It was also he who had challenged me to a drinking bout. Although I had lost, he told me that I had a streak of greatness in me but that I must accept the challenges of fate. Remembering, I answered, "And a fateful feast that was. It was the feast that changed my life." I hesitated and then, seeing his interest, I added, "Upon my return in a drunken state, my mother commissioned me to seek apprenticeship in Tsang."

"She was displeased or pleased?" the peasant asked, closing one eye as he spoke, as if to sharpen his image of me.

Had he been anyone else, I would have belittled him for asking such an obvious question, but the look in his eyes made me answer him straightly. "Displeased, sir!"

"Because you drank a bit too much chang beer?"

"Because I was drunk instead of fulfilling my family responsibility," I confessed.

"I see."

I shrugged my shoulders. "It was a good feast, anyway," I said. "I had a grand time."

"I'm glad," the driver said, gazing at me. "Do you remember me, boy?"

I smiled. "Indeed I do, sir, although at first, I admit, I didn't. You were the one who challenged me to a drinking bout. It was you who won."

"Yes, well," the driver said, proudly cocking his head. His expression was more serious now. "Should I try to set things right with your family?"

"No," I answered quickly. "I must go to Tsang."

"By what route then?"

"This road."

"No, boy. This road winds forever. It is made for the cart. You have seen how unnerving it can be with traffic." The peasant hesitated, then continued. "I know a faster and better route to Tsang, if you are interested."

"Of course," I answered gratefully.

"See that forest ahead?" the driver asked, pointing in the distance off to the right.

"Yes, sir."

"If you are willing to travel through it, it will cut four days from your journey and be a more pleasant trip besides."

I had never journeyed through a forest. I had been told of the wildlife—boar, snakes and panda bear, leopards and monkeys— and believed it too dangerous.

"It is not the frightful place you might think," the driver said, as though sensing my feelings. "There is a clean trail through this forest and most of the wildlife is reasonably tame. They are used to seeing man. At least they have never bothered me."

"You have traveled through the forest?" I asked.

"Indeed…four times. Two times on my way to Tsu and two times in return to Tsang," the driver said.

"You do not live in Tsu?" I asked, surprised.

"No, boy, I live near Tsang. I am visiting in Tsu."

My previous fascination for the man returned. I was curious about his activities in Tsu and would have questioned him, except that the uneven load of bundles on my back reminded me of the urgency of my journey. I shifted them uneasily. The man watched me. "And you were not threatened in the forest?" I asked.

"Never threatened," the driver said. "I'll tell you something about animals, boy." He paused, keenly eyeing me as I still stood in the ditch. "Climb out of there and I will tell you."

I climbed out of the ditch and moved to the side of the cart nearest the driver.

The driver shifted the reins from hand to hand, gazing first past me and then directly at me. My attention was riveted on him. "Animals *think* they have to fight to survive. Not to say that they really think like you or me. Animals react and the mainstay of their reactions is fear. If they are around something that is afraid, they feel threatened by that fear, but if there is no fear in a person or animal who comes near, they turn their heads the other way. The plain truth is that if you are not afraid, chances are they won't be afraid and they won't attack, as long as you don't accidentally startle them. A leopard won't strike unless he smells fear or is hungry." The driver paused, chuckling to himself as though he had said something funny. "Animals have to be half-starved to want to eat a man. They plain don't like the taste of us."

"Then why would an animal attack a man?" I asked.

The man smiled with tight lips. "One day in the low country," he said, "I was confronted by a rhinoceros. The beast stared at me. He became aggressive at precisely the moment I allowed my fear to get out of hand. You know, when a cold chill runs up your back. That chill is fear. The rhinoceros sensed it and charged."

"What did you do?"

"I climbed a tree. I was lucky there was one to climb," the driver said, shaking his head at the memory.

"You are sure your fear made the rhinoceros charge at you?" I asked.

"I have had other experiences to prove it," the peasant said.

I was thoughtful and did not speak.

"You will be all right if you remember to control your fear," the cart driver said. "Follow this road until you come to the trail into the forest." He paused, pointing ahead. "You can't miss it." He motioned to me to move behind him so that he could pass without forcing me back into the ditch. "Have a safe journey," he said. The farmer gave the reins a snap and the yak began to move.

When I arrived at the forest of pine trees, I immediately saw the opening, a narrow trail that entered into the center of the pines and disappeared into the thick of them. I stood staring at the entrance, uncertain, thinking about what the cart driver had told me. The trail through the forest would shorten my journey by four days and I had nothing to fear except the feeling of fear itself. I did not know if I could control my fear. I had never put myself to the test. Yet if I stayed with the road, I was liable to meet with another cart accident or, worse, become the victim of robbers. But then there was also the chance that I would meet with a cart going to Tsang and would be offered a lift. It also occurred to me that, should one cart meet another going in the opposite direction, the delay could be a long one.

I stepped into the forest and hurriedly followed the path, which disappeared into the heart of it. At first I was tense and apprehensive, looking in every direction as I moved forward with unsteady steps. Then, gradually, I became accustomed to the unevenness of the ground and the smell of sweet pines and I began to relax. There was calmness in the forest and the presence of it comforted me. I tried to imagine my first meeting with the great sorcerer of Tsang. All I knew of the man were tales of his power, that he could assume any form or shape he desired. Some men claimed he changed himself into animals in order to roam freely without being detected by those he did not wish to know him. Others said he moved in an invisible presence, without form of any kind, that he was the presence of worldly turmoil in that he assumed the rage of the thunder, the strike of the lightening, and the hail of the hailstorms. I could not imagine what such a man would look like. Certainly he must be powerfully built in order to assume the greatness of the power foretold of him.

The narrow trail through the pines suddenly opened into a green field. Everywhere there were sweetly scented rhododendron. Monkeys swung from their sweeping branches. Through the center of the grove was a fast-running brook. The water cascaded over round grey stones. Tiny yellow and purple flowers intermingled with the grasses, which overlapped the banks. It was a beautiful sight and one that fully captured my attention. I had never seen anything like it. It wasn't until a monkey crept up behind me and gave my robe a quick jerk that I returned to my senses. The monkey ran off as I turned around but I could see that there were many of them, eyeing me with curiosity.

I again thought of the sorcerer of Tsang, wondering at the difference between a sorcerer and a yogi. Lama Kataka had told Zesay of the powers of a great yogi and how one could live on little or no food or sleep. The Lama had also recounted tales of yogis assuming any form desired. What then was the difference? Were they not both men of power? Both had power, it seemed, to destroy and protect and yet I doubted that a yogi would use the power to destroy. Perhaps that was the difference. It had to be the reason that my mother had never asked for Lama Kataka's prayers.

A twig snapped in the distance. I turned to look in the direction of the sound. I became aware of a faint whistling. I waited, listening, staring into the bushes. Suddenly the bushes parted and a young man about my age appeared. He smiled at me as though he had expected to find me. "I hope I did not frighten you," the boy called out.

I waited without answering, wondering if I knew him.

"I heard about your journey in Nyang," the boy said, approaching, holding a small package in front of him. "Since I, too, was on my way to Tsang, I stopped at your mother's house. She told me that you had already left." He paused, standing before me. "Your mother sends this message," he said, handing it to me. "When I told her that I was on my way to Tsang, she sent me to join you. The cart driver told me you would be taking this route."

I accepted the package, studying the boy curiously. Because of my family's position in the village I had not had much association with boys my own age. I had been considered a social outcast and, except for peasants, few ever sought my company. This young man was obviously of noble birth. His clothes were fine and he had a look of wealth about him. He was about my age and build, although his shoulders were not quite as broad nor did his face have the same prominent features. Instead, his forehead was low. His nose was round, almost clownlike, and his chin was nearly absent, slipping directly into his neck.

"My name is Thither," the boy said, grinning. "I come from Ngari-Dol." He bowed politely.

I bowed in return, recalling that I had heard of the boy's family. They had a fine reputation and much land and money.

"Could you use a traveling companion?" the boy asked.

"You are welcome," I responded. I had not been looking forward to the long days and nights alone. I asked him if he had ever been to Tsang and what his purpose was there. The small package from my mother began to weigh in my hand.

"I, too, am seeking the sorcerer, only my purpose is different," Thither said. "I wish to learn something of black magic to better understand religion. For many years, I studied with our village Lama, but still, I have many unanswered questions."

I saw now that although the boy's features were not handsome, he had a keen look in his eyes.

"I wish to be a Lama someday," Thither said, "but not an ignorant one. There is so much ignorance in my village, so much superstition." He hesitated, noticing that I was examining the package he had brought from my mother. "Go ahead and open it," Thither said. "We will have plenty of time to get acquainted later."

I went to a large rock next to the stream and sat down. Gently, I untied the twine holding the package intact and allowed the thick paper to unwrap itself. Inside was my mother's prize turquoise. It had been given to her by my father on their wedding day. It was all she had left of her estate. I could not imagine her parting with it. Inside was a note.

> *My Dear Only Son:*
> Guard the turquoise well. It is to be your gift to the black magician in return for his instruction. Its value is so great that he will not be able to deny you his knowledge.
> We miss you greatly. Already your wicked aunt and uncle are outraged by your leaving and have demanded that I return to work in the rice fields to fill your place.
> *Your loving mother,*
> *Nyangtsha Kargyen*

I clutched the turquoise in the palm of my hand and sat staring at the letter. My eyes clouded with tears. My sentimental feelings were mixed with anger. I hated my evil aunt and uncle, not so much because they had stolen from my family, but because their greed was never satisfied. They were draining my mother of life.

"We could camp here," Thither said, interrupting my thoughts. "It would give us a chance to become acquainted and to discuss our journey to Tsang."

Had it not been for my sudden anger, I would have agreed, but instead I quickly rose to my feet. "There are still several hours of daylight," I said. "I am going on. You stay here if you like." I paused to knot my mother's turquoise, along with the letter, securely into the pocket of my robe, then turned and hurried up the trail toward Tsang.

Thither hurried to catch up.

When nightfall finally came, we were at the edge of the forest. I would have liked to continue on into the open, but the moon was dark and travel was impossible. I quickly looked around to make sure it was safe before I spread out my blanket. I did not speak to Thither but was aware that he silently spread out his blanket nearby.

Morning came suddenly. I was the first to rise. I went a few feet from the camp to relieve myself and then returned. Plucking at the strings of my traveling sack, I finally opened it and withdrew a portion of dried meat and cooked rice. I scooped the rice up in my hand and quickly fed it into my open mouth.

Thither awoke at the smell of food. "Good morning," he called out, stretching himself and sitting up. He looked at me and grinned, watching me eat hungrily, using my fingers to shovel the food into my mouth. "I have some noodles and boarmeat. Would you like some?" he asked.

I paused to look at Thither. The preparation of noodles required ingredients that my family seldom had and boarmeat was considered a delicacy. My own meat was squirrel and rat and, while nourishing, they lacked the succulence of boar.

"I have plenty," Thither added, knowing that he had appealed to my culinary senses. "We could share my food until it runs out and then eat yours."

I did not speak but slowly nodded my head approvingly. It was a generous offer.

"My father shot the boar while hunting outside your village," Thither said. "There was quite some competition for it. Other hunters were about and several of them had spotted the beast. My father had to be swift but he had to pay handsomely in transporting the boar home. The other hunters took a portion of the kill, as well as gold for their help."

"Did you assist in the hunt?" I asked. My curiosity drew me from silence. I had never hunted boar and had heard that it was a risky adventure.

"No," Thither said, hesitating. He smiled. "Much to the displeasure of my father, I am not much for hunting, at least not for the sport of it. I wish instead to be a man of God."

I stared at Thither but said nothing. I thought of Zesay and how my beloved would react to Thither. She would like him, I knew. I bit into the semi-soft, fleshy boarmeat and slowly chewed. It was delicious, better than any meat I had had in a long while.

Thither offered his wooden container of noodles. I wiped my greasy hands on my blanket and dipped my fingers into the bowl, lifting a biteful of noodles to my mouth. Although cold and soggy, they were delicious.

"My sister made the noodles," Thither said, "Not only is she a beautiful jewel but her talents are many." I dug my fingers into the noodles again and ate hungrily. "Is your sister a good cook?" he asked with a full mouth.

I stopped eating and looked past Thither. In my mind's eye I could see my sister Peta, remembering how, when I last saw her, she was standing in front of the cooking pots, tears streaming down her face. Suddenly the rise of anger I had felt the night before crept forward again. I lowered my eyes, and gazing at the boarmeat I held in the other hand, I tore off a piece of the gray flesh with my teeth. I could feel Thither staring at me. Like him, I was nearly a man and yet still a boy. We were past the age of tears and complaint and yet not quite prepared for the burden of family responsibility. I was sure from his carefree manner that this family did not expect much of him, whereas I was all that my mother and sister had. They expected me to avenge them and to reclaim our stolen family fortune. It was a well-told tale, not only in Nyang where I lived, but in neighboring villages as well. Thither undoubtedly knew how people pitied me, how they gave me strong drink as an escape. It was rumored that I was a drunkard, but it was not true.

We ate quietly. The edge of my anger gradually subsided. Finally I wiped my mouth and looked around. Streams of sunlight poured through the tall pines. I raised myself up on my hands and moved my seat a few feet to the left, sitting in the middle of the warm light. The golden heat, coupled with a full stomach, made me relax and I turned my head to Thither, who was still busy eating and did not seem to notice. I began to wonder about my companion and the quirk of fate that had brought him into my life. There was something comforting about Thither and I was glad that he had joined me.

Thither put his food back into storage and tied the wraps of the thin-skinned container. He rolled his blanket and tied one end to the other. When he had finished, he looked over at me. I smiled. The sun warmed me in a comforting way. I tilted my face up to it; the rays of the sun washed over me. After awhile I lowered my head and saw that Thither was bowed before me. I was astonished and quickly turned to see if someone else had come up behind me, but there was no one. I turned again to my traveling companion. "Thither, why are you bowing?" I asked. The sun rays moved past me to the trunk of the tree. I was no longer in the sunlight.

Thither looked up and slowly rose to his knees. He looked at the tree where the sunlight was now hitting and then back at me. "Seeing you in the sunlight reminded me of the Buddha," he answered softly, with embarrassment.

I eyed my companion curiously. "And who is Buddha?" I asked. "I have never heard of him."

"My Lama told me of the great yogi Marpa, who lives in the village of Nar in the heart of Tsang Valley. He is the translator of Buddhist doctrine. He brought the words and teachings of Buddha to Tibet from India."

"But who is Buddha?" I asked again.

"Not *who* really," Thither answered, "but *what*. Buddha is a term for higher consciousness."

"Well, for certain, I am not Buddha then," I said sarcastically. "I am on a mission of hate and revenge. I seek the highest of the lowest consciousness, not the highest of high." I could feel the anger flare in me and flash through my eyes.

Thither averted his eyes to avoid my bolt of negative feeling, then he looked up again. "I wasn't really bowing to you," he explained, "but to a memory. After the Lama told me of the Buddha, I had a dream. I was walking on a hillside through a forest," he hesitated, looking around, "like this forest. As I was hiking up the hillside, I came upon a huge rock. On it was painted the image of a faceless man. His body was enveloped in light. When later I told the Lama about the dream, he explained that I had traveled in spirit to Tsang Valley and had seen the painted rock that guards the entranceway to the village of Nar. He told me that the image painted on the rock is the Buddha and that it signifies higher consciousness. He also told me that the Buddha is wrapped in light because light is the manifestation of that consciousness." He hesitated again, studying me. "So you see I wasn't really bowing to you," he continued, "but to the memory of Buddha. Your form, caught in the sunlight, brought the memory to life."

I was embarrassed. I did not wish to argue with Thither and, to show it, I quickly shrugged my shoulders, as if to say I didn't care. I rose to my feet, thinking about his story of the rock painting and the village of Nar. The story had disturbed me for some reason that wasn't clear. "Are you going to Nar instead of Tsang?" I asked, turning away wishing that I hadn't asked. I reached for my blanket and began shaking it. Bits of bark and pine needles flew away from it. Thither did not answer. I folded the blanket into a neat square and tied it with straps of hide. Then I tied my food pouch to it and raised the bundle to my back. When I was ready to go, I turned to Thither, who was shifting his bundles uncomfortably, positioning them on his back. "Well, is that what you intend to do?" I asked again.

Thither gazed at me with a faraway look in his eyes. He shook his head and held out the palm of his hands as if to say he didn't know.

I stared at him. It was none of my business what Thither did. Why then did it disturb me?

Once we left the pine forest and headed into the mountain range, our attention shifted to more physical matters. The air was thinning as we headed upward and, when finally we reached that spot on our journey that was twice the altitude of our own villages, we found that we hiked less and rested more often. We did not know how high we would have to climb. The pass wound to the other side of the mountain into Tsang, not going over it, but by moving around it, and the adjustment to the height left us often exhausted. Some days we were not able to travel at all.

I was frustrated by the delay but could do nothing about it. Often I would sit for hours studying the parchment map my mother had given me. It was not the distance that was so great as it was the perils of trying to hurry the distance. The more I tried to push on, the slower we seemed to move. I watched the behavior of my companion. Although suffering a similar degree of exhaustion, Thither wasn't disturbed by it. When I tried to push on, he let me go on by myself. Later he would catch up by the mere fact that I would have collapsed not far ahead.

Food was running low and water was becoming increasingly difficult to find. Thither's boarmeat and noodles were gone and we now ate the dried squirrel and rat meat that I had brought. When that was gone we would eat the grains my mother had packed. Occasionally, we would come upon a small pool of water, seepage from a spring deep inside the rock, and pause to fill our bellies with it.

One day, after traveling a long distance without finding water, I remembered something Peta and I talked about and burst out laughing. Thither found me, alone and laughing to myself. I was laughing so hard that tears rolled from my eyes and streamed down my cheeks.

"What's so funny?" Thither asked, leaning against a rock.

I stared at him with a blank face and then burst out laughing again.

"What is it?" Thither asked again. He was laughing himself without knowing why.

I paused. "When Peta and I were very young," I said, sucking in a breath of thin mountain air, "we worried about what we would do if ever we were without food or drink." I hesitated laughing and coughing, gasping for breath.

"And what happened?" Thither asked.

"Peta said, "Well, don't worry about it, my brother..." I paused, laughing, unable to get the words out.

"Go on," Thither prodded.

"Peta said, 'It's okay, we can always drink our own piss.'" I suddenly became very sober. "We can, you know." I said.

Thither stared at me, a look of surprise on his face, then he burst out laughing.

"What's wrong with you?" I asked, feeling oddly like it was his joke instead of mine.

"Don't you know?"

"No, I don't know!" I said. I was suddenly annoyed.

"It's a good idea," Thither said.

"What is?"

"Drinking our piss," Thither said. "Don't you know?"

"Know what?" I demanded.

"Hunters drink their piss all the time," Thither said. "If you run out of water, there is nothing else you can do."

There was no doubt that Thither was serious and I could not help feeling naïve and embarrassed. "Did you ever drink your piss?" I asked.

Thither nodded. "My father made me do it once so that I would accept the rules of survival. Basically, there is only one rule and that is to do what needs to be done."

"Was it awful?"

"No," Thither said, laughing at my seriousness. "How can it be awful if it is only your own body fluid? It might be awful if it was someone else's body fluid you had to drink." He paused, seeing that my expression had turned thoughtful. After a moment, he suggested that we continue on our way.

As we neared Tsang, the journey became increasingly more difficult and hazardous. Contrary to our fears about being thirsty, there was plenty of drinking water. The hazard now was that, as the narrow trail wound around the mountain, it became steeper and narrower, so narrow in fact that we had to cling to the soft sandstone walls and inch our way upward. Once, Thither's foot slipped off the side and he lost his balance. He would have fallen to his death if I hadn't been quick in grabbing his arm.

There was little time to rest because there was nowhere to sit. To take a break from the exhausting climb, we had to turn our backs to the cliff wall and lean against it. It was then that we would truly see the endless range of mountains around us.

"Sometimes I feel that I am dead," I said, gazing out to the mountains around us.

"In what way?" Thither asked.

"Life has become so unreal, so dreamlike," I answered. "Perhaps, instead of feeling dead, I am really feeling that I am dreaming. Perhaps we will wake up from this sleeping experience soon."

"The feeling comes from the high, thin air." Thither said. "The Lama in my village, upon hearing of my journey, told me to expect it. He also told me that when the feeling came, I would experience the most dangerous part of the journey."

"Why is that?" I asked.

"The feeling that nothing is real," Thither said, "makes it easy to become careless."

I thought of Zesay, remembering the smooth lines of her neck and how I had desired her. I thought, too, of my mother and reached in my side pocket to make sure the turquoise was still there. "How high do you believe we are?" I asked.

Thither stared into the great abyss that reached endlessly before us. "The Lama Kataka explained it this way," he said, holding out his foot to me. "He told me that if my foot could be stretched sixteen thousand times, I would have an idea of the height I would have to climb. He warned that the air becomes so thin that men have plunged to their death, feeling that they could fly. He also said that a man's mind begins to see things that do not exist when one is not accustomed to the altitude."

"Well, at least that has not happened," I said, grinning. "We are still in sound mind."

Toward nightfall the path widened into a road again and we saw that beneath us was a lush green valley enclosed by mountains. It was not a wide valley. From where we stood above it, it seemed that one could walk it in a day's time, but it was very long. The length of the valley stretched out as far as the eye could see, rounding the bend of the mountain we were climbing. I drew the parchment map from inside my robe and studied it. Thither stood speechlessly, gazing into the valley. I had the sensation that I had been there before, even though I knew that it could not be so.

"It is Tsang Valley," I said, holding out the map to Thither and pointing to the spot.

Thither nodded as though he had already known it.

I looked again at the map, seeing that the city of Tsang was not the same as the valley. Tsang was a province, and according to the map, it also joined the province of U. The city of Tsang was on the other side of the mountain, far to the left of the valley. I turned to Thither. "The black magician is here, somewhere in this province," I said, tapping the map with my forefinger. I did not say anymore about the valley floor, hoping that my companion had not decided to go there instead.

Thither stared down at the green valley floor. He told me that the village of Nar, where the yogi Marpa lived, was down there. It was easy to see that he longed to go there. I became uneasy watching him but could think of nothing to say to attract his attention. Standing there, my thoughts wandered back to the cart driver. He had said that his home was near Tsang. Then gradually I became aware that it was growing dark, that the sun would soon disappear behind the hills. I suggested that we stay the night where we were. He eagerly agreed.

When morning came, Thither was the first to rise. He began to sing as he quickly wrapped his blanket about our meager supply of food. He was joyful, free, and easy, as light as a feather, whereas my head throbbed and I felt nauseated. I watched as Thither went to the edge of the cliff, looking out into the valley. Painfully, I rose to my feet, moaning about the pain in my head. My body was sore from many nights of sleeping on the damp, cold rock and I could not stand up straight. I rubbed my back with one hand and held my head with the other. "How is it that you sing when I am so miserable?" I called out. "Is your body free from pain?"

Thither turned around and faced me. He appeared distant at first and then walked over to me. "You are experiencing altitude sickness," he said. "Stand up straight and I will see what I can do."

I forced myself to stand erect, lowering my hands to my sides.

Thither went around to the back of me. "Take in a slow, deep breath," he instructed. "Then exhale slowly, through your nostrils. Do this ten times and then stand absolutely still, breathing normally."

I was in no condition to argue and so I followed Thither's instructions. Meanwhile, Thither kneaded his thumbs in between the vertebrae in my back. When he had finished, he stood back, waiting until I showed signs of breathing normally. "How do you feel?" he asked.

"Better," I said uncertainly, turning to face Thither and asking how it was that he felt so well.

"My sickness is expressed in feeling gay and light," Thither said, suddenly appearing dreamy and distant, as he had when he first turned from the edge of the cliff. "I could be like the idiots who jump off the cliff, believing they can fly."

I eyed my friend curiously. "Strange that our reactions are so opposite," I said.

"Not so strange," Thither answered, shaking his head. "Not when you consider the difference in our missions."

"Meaning?" I asked.

"You come to learn to get revenge." Thither said. "I come to ready myself for higher knowledge. It is only natural that I feel lighter and filled with joy." Then he smiled and good-naturedly patted me on the back. "Isn't it time we headed into Tsang?" he asked.

"The feeling that nothing is real makes it easy to become careless."

CHAPTER THREE
THE ARRIVAL

Tsang was a surprise and different from any place either of us had visited. As a province, it was the hub of officialdom. Geographically, it was a separate state, isolated from other populated areas by the natural terrain. The buildings were sunk into the cliffs, giving them the appearance of being fortresses. Finely dressed people, wearing silk brocaded garments, hurried about the streets with bundles under their arms. It was obvious that more than the basics of living took place here. Passersby entered and exited the busy structures in a businesslike manner. Occasionally, one would pause and, believing us to be beggars, offer us a coin, which we refused.

I glanced down at the new robe my mother had made me and then at Thither's. Our garments were badly soiled and it was easy to see why we were regarded as beggars. Whenever we paused along the cobblestone streets to seek direction, people avoided us, sometimes backing away and, at other times, pushing ahead of us. We received many stares and backward glances.

I shifted the pack on my back uneasily and looked about the network of cobblestone streets and public buildings. Thither stood silently next to me. The altitude sickness was still with me. My head pounded from lack of oxygen, although I did not let on that I felt it. "Did Lama Kataka tell you what to expect in Tsang?" I asked in a quiet voice.

"He made little mention of Tsang Province, only of Tsang Valley," Thither said, staring down the streets. It seemed that he was searching his memory for something the Lama had said, but he said nothing.

The rough clattering of animal hooves came up behind us and both of us spun on our heels.

A yak and rider came trotting up to us and stopped. The rider, a big man in a grey brocade suit with a red sash, drew in the reins. He sat motionless, staring boldly down on us. "Where are you headed?" he asked in a firm voice.

Both of us hesitated. We had never seen such a striking figure on the back of a yak. "Yarlung-Kyorpo," I finally answered.

The man in grey glared at us from the yak, shifting his weight as the shaggy beast moved restlessly under him. He looked first at me and then at Thither. "Are you going to Yarlung-Kyorpo as well?" he asked.

"I am," Thither answered. "We have just crossed the mountains and are now unsure of the way."

"From what village are you?" the rider asked.

"Ngari-Dol," Thither answered uneasily. "My friend is from Nyang."

The yak moved again and the big man in grey adjusted his seat on the soft sheepskin saddle. He drew in a deep breath as though deciding how he would handle us. "Yarlung-Kyorpo is not a place many wish to visit," he said. "Are you sure you wish to go to Yarlung-Kyorpo and not some other village?"

I reached into my robe and withdrew the parchment map I carried and held it up to the rider. "It is the place marked on my map," I answered courteously.

The man on the yak hesitated.

Thither glanced up and down the streets. Those on foot paused to stare at us as they passed. It was obvious that the rider in grey with the red sash was an officer of the law.

"It is not a place for young men of high purpose," the officer said firmly.

"It is our destination, sir," I answered with determination.

The man returned the map to me. "Go to it then," he said. "You will find the village you seek up over the next ridge. Follow this street to the end." He paused pointing the direction. "It will lead you there. But before going that way, consider that you are safe here in Tsang, even if not welcome. In Yarlung-Kyorpo, you may be both unsafe and unwelcome. To go there speaks for itself."

A cold chill traveled up my spine and I lowered my eyes, sensing a like reaction from Thither. Then, trying to appear undisturbed, I looked up at the rider. "Thank you for your concern, sir, and thank you for the direction." I quickly nudged Thither and the two of us began walking in the direction the rider had shown.

We could feel the man on the yak-back looking after us. Finally we heard his animal trot away.

"What do you make of him?" Thither asked, turning to look after the man and beast.

"You mean his concern?" I asked, uneasily.

He nodded.

I didn't answer right away. I didn't want to make an issue of it. We were both uneasy enough. "We had better keep our wits about us," I answered finally.

At the end of the street, there was an inn. Sweet smells of roasting meat rushed out to greet us. We paused and then saw the trail we had been told to travel to Yarlung-Kyorpo. It seemed to follow the mountains.

We both hesitated, looking in all directions, and then at the inn again. On street level was a stable, but just above it was a window and out of it came laughter as well as the smell of delicious foods.

Thither turned to me and grinned. "Let us rest here before we continue," he said anxiously.

I became suddenly apprehensive, staring thoughtfully past Thither. I was not sure that I should. A part of me told me to push on.

"The man on yak-back told us we would be safe here in Tsang," Thither prodded.

I looked first at the inn and then at Thither. He was thin and drawn in appearance, as though the blood had been slowly drained from him. The journey had taken its toll and I was sure that it showed on me as well. My head ached so much that I could feel it pounding in my ears. It was absurd to think that we should continue on without proper food and rest. Playfully, I crossed my eyes and grinned back at Thither.

Thither laughed, playfully bumping me with the butt of his hand and nearly knocking me off-balance. Quickly he grabbed me, steadying me.

We began to laugh. After a moment, Thither prodded again, "Milarepa, let's go in."

Although a part of me had already given in, I still hesitated. We were so close to Yarlung-Kyorpo, yet my body felt in such disrepair. I wasn't sure that I could continue without food and rest. An image of my mother's face haunted me, nudging me to go on, to reach the village of Yarlung-Kyorpo quickly, at all costs. Yet if I died along the way, or worse, if I arrived in such a confused state that the Lama rejected me, my life and journey would be in vain. I would have failed my mother and myself—Peta and Zesay too.

"I have a good supply of gold coins given to me by my family for the journey," Thither said, prodding. "I will gladly share them with you. They can buy us food and rest in this comfortable place until our bodies adjust to the altitude."

I stared at Thither. Had I not been in so much discomfort, I would have argued that I, too, had gold. My mother had given me two gold coins. But I knew that to bring it up would have been a matter of foolish pride, that those gold coins really were to be paid to the Lama Yungtun-Trogyal, along with the turquoise, in exchange for his knowledge. I knew, too, that if I insisted on going into the mountains, Thither was in no condition to continue. I did not know what difficulties we would find ahead. "All right," I said finally. "Let us recuperate here."

Thither went quickly to the inn door and pounded on it, standing impatiently, waiting for a reply. After a moment, the door opened and a woman looked out at us. She was dressed in earth-colored robes. Her hair was tied back from her face, and ornaments hung from her ears. She hesitated, sizing us up, then motioned to us to enter.

Once inside, we were met by the woman's husband. Thither explained that we were travelers, unaccustomed to the altitude of Tsang and that we required a place to rest before we continued on our journey. The proprietor nodded without question, as though he had heard the story many times. "Can you pay?" was all he asked.

Thither reached into the inside pocket of his tattered robe and withdrew a handful of gold coins, showing them to the man.

The man quickly eyed the gold coins and then us. "You will both require a week's recuperation," he said expertly. "I can give you food, a clean room with a window and a comfortable bed on the next floor, including use of our bath. The price is two gold coins each for one week." He looked first at Thither and then at me, waiting for a reply.

We were in no condition to haggle over price. Thither handed the man four gold coins and bowed gratefully. I bowed as well.

"If you would like fresh clothes, I can supply them for one gold coin apiece," the man added quickly.

Thither glanced down at his very tattered clothing and then at mine. It was obvious that in order to make a favorable impression on the Lama Yungtun-Trogyal, we would have to appear more presentable. "All right," he said, handing the proprietor two more gold coins. I tried to stop him by staying his hand but Thither pushed my hand out of the way. "May we bathe and then eat before we go to our room?"

The proprietor lifted the gold coins from Thither's hand and nodded, motioning to the woman to lead us.

The innkeeper's wife reached to a sideboard to put some oil into a lamp. When she had finished, she rubbed a flint onto a piece of rock and lit it, waving us to follow. She led us to a hallway and down a narrow flight of stairs, into a semi-dark room. Nightfall was approaching and little light came in through the window. By the strong dung smell, it was easy to tell that the stable was directly behind the next wall.

The woman put the lamp on the dirt floor and immediately the room brightened. In front of us was a pool of water deep enough to swim in where we were to bathe, and off to the side, was an oven filled with glowing coals. The innkeeper's wife reached for a pair of tongs that hung over the oven and lifted some large rocks from the coals. One by one, she threw the rocks in the bathing pool. After a few moments, she reached down and tested the water with her hand and then returned to the oven to add a few more hot stones. Finally, when the water was warm enough, she motioned that we should remove our clothes and get into it. She left the room.

We quickly undressed and slipped into the warm water. The feeling of it was comforting and, for some moments, we enjoyed the pleasure without movement. Gradually, the water began to cool, and we washed ourselves.

The innkeeper's wife entered again, carrying thin woven cloths for us to dry ourselves and held up a pair of grey pants and a tunic for each of us. They were made of cotton and were nowhere as fine as those we had been wearing, yet we nodded gratefully.

I splashed more water on my face and dunked my hair one last time before drawing myself from the pool. I was about to dry myself when I saw the woman reach for our old clothes. "No, stop!" I called, hurrying to snatch them from her hands.

The woman was startled and backed up, bowing apologetically. She again left the room.

Thither pulled himself from the pool and began to dry himself, occasionally glancing at me as I adjusted the baggy grey cotton clothes the woman had left us. As first I had some difficulty keeping the pants up under the shirt, until I tied the rope from my tattered robe about my waist. "You have lost much weight, my friend," Thither said, beginning to pull on his own suit of cotton greys. He quickly realized that his were much too big as well. He removed the sash from his old tunic and tied it about his waist. "Imagine paying a gold coin for these clothes," he said, although it was obvious that he was so affected by the altitude that he did not really care.

I looked at Thither but said nothing. My head felt as though someone had filled it with rocks and they rubbed one against the other whenever I moved or spoke. Thinking, it seemed, made my head ever more sensitive.

We gathered up our old clothing and rolled it into a ball. I was especially careful how I rolled mine, checking the inside pockets as I did, feeling the turquoise my mother had given me. We went into the hall. The innkeeper's wife was waiting for us. "Your food has already been brought to your room," she said, bowing slightly.

We followed her to the second floor. To the right, at the top of the stairs, she opened a door. Inside were two yak fleeces spread out as mattresses on the floor, and next to each, a wooden tray was heaped with food. The aroma of boarmeat immediately caught our attention.

The woman entered and went to the far wall where a skin was hanging. Touching it, she turned to us, nodding, then pulled the skin back from the wall, revealing a window. The dim light of a full moon came into the room. She let go of the skin. It fell back into place, concealing the opening from the cool night air. "You need anything, you ask," she said pleasantly, "otherwise we do not disturb you." She placed the oil lamp between the two yak skins, bowed, and left the room, closing the door behind her.

Both Thither and I went to the soft mattresses and sat down. I felt the skin with my hand. It was brownish in color and the texture of it, though soft, was unlike the sheepskin I slept on at home. It was thick, shaggy, and slightly rough to the touch. I placed my bundle of old clothes and my pack at the head of the skin and turned my attention to the plate of food next to me. Thither was already eating. There was boarmeat, bread, and a root vegetable, which neither of us could identify. It had a slightly tart taste but it was enjoyable. We ate everything on our plates. Our hunger satisfied, we stretched out on the yak-skin mattresses, securing our belongings by using them as pillows, and fell fast asleep.

When next I awoke, it was dark in the room. The lamp had gone out. I was slightly chilly and pulled up one of the extra skins the woman had left until it was high around my neck. Thither was asleep and well-covered. I lowered my head onto the folded robe my mother had made me and, realizing that my head no longer ached, slipped gratefully back into a deep sleep.

I awoke again sometime in the night. I arose from my sleeping fleece and went to the latrine on the far wall, listening to the sounds of my urine trickling down the mud-lined slot that led to the street below. When I had finished, I went to the window, lifted the skin covering and looked out. The street was bathed in semi-darkness, light enough to see anyone who might have been walking in the area, but there was no one. It was quiet and yet strangely so. Here in the city there were sounds different from the silence of being alone in the mountains. I looked at the sky to see if the moon was visible, but could not see it. Was it full or was it dark? I could not remember.

A strange feeling came over me. I had slept outdoors on the trail for three weeks, had marked the phases of the moon in my mind, and now I couldn't remember if it was full or not. It was absurd, as though I had suddenly lost touch with the world. How long had I been asleep? Had fatigue and the high, thin air taken a toll on my senses?

Thither groaned and I spun on my heels. I saw my companion lying there, his arms raised over his head, stretching. "Ah, I see that you too are awake," Thither said in a slurred voice.

Thither turned on his stomach and propped his head with his hands, looking up at me as I stood next to the open window. The night air had a chill to it but it was not really cold. Quickly, he glanced around the small room as though remembering where he was. He looked up at me again. "Is it daybreak?" he asked.

I did not know what to answer. I did not know.

"Is there anything wrong?" Thither asked.

I dropped the window covering and went back to my fleece to lie down. "No, nothing," I said, uncertain. I felt the robe my mother had made me. A lump in the center of it told me that the turquoise was still there.

"Did you sleep?" Thither asked.

"Yes," I answered, "only I do not know how long."

Thither sat up and looked at me. "What do you mean?"

"I don't know if it is now day or night," I answered, hesitating, "or even what day it is."

Thither laughed. A sudden pang of hunger made his stomach rumble. "Do you think anyone in the household is up and about? I could use a little food."

"I have heard nothing," I said.

Thither scrambled to his feet and hurried to the door, opening it. He meant to listen for sounds of people moving about, but his foot tapped a hard object. Looking down, he saw a tray of food waiting outside the door. He reached down and picked it up, carrying it back inside. "Look what I found," he said happily. He placed the food on the floor between the mattresses and motioned for me to dig in. Then he helped himself.

I sat up and reached toward the tray. I sank my teeth into a tough piece of dried meat. It tasted like squirrel but I doubted that squirrels lived at such high altitude. It was probably rat. There was bread as well, which I enjoyed more. The thick dough seemed to give me a feeling of strength and it reminded me of Peta's bread. My sister always saved me the end pieces. I liked those best because they were crunchy. The memory made me feel very, very warm and yet lonely. I had the feeling that it would be a very long time before I saw Peta again.

"We may have slept for days," Thither said lightly.

I looked up, sensing it to be true, that we had slept for more than a day. I felt rested. My head no longer pounded and my legs no longer ached.

"I feel great," Thither said, smiling. "How about you?"

I nodded. I stretched my limbs out to the side. "I am ready to travel," I said earnestly. I rose from my fleece and went to the window again, pulling back the skin that covered it. It was daybreak. The sun was rising just over the horizon and the streets were filling with rays of light. I tied the window covering back and returned to my fleece, gazing at Thither. Light was filling our room.

"We have paid for a week's lodging," Thither said, studying the firm expression on my face. "The proprietor said it would take us that long to become accustomed to the altitude. It would not be wise for us to appear before the black magician in a weakened state."

I studied my companion. It was obvious that he was not anxious to continue and I didn't blame him. He was seeking the sorcerer for a milder purpose. "It will be an easy hike for me," I said. "I feel strong and ready and it is urgent that I get there. You can join me when you are ready. Meanwhile, I will tell the sorcerer of your coming."

Thither had appeared relieved at my conclusion. I knew he wanted to stay the week, to visit the sights of Tsang, and to learn what he could of the city. He was not in a hurry to meet the sorcerer. Smiling, Thither replied, "All right. You go on ahead. I will catch up with you."

Thither accompanied me downstairs. The innkeeper and his wife greeted us.

"I see you finally awaken," the innkeeper said.

"Finally?" I asked.

"You arrived morning before last," the innkeeper's wife said smiling. "Your sleep was longer than most, but I think you have traveled a greater distance than most men who visit us." She paused, seeing the surprised expressions on our faces. "We are pleased that you are feeling rested," she said again.

We bowed politely, then Thither explained that I would continue on while he remained behind for the remainder of the week.

The innkeeper and his wife looked at me but did not try to discourage me. I thanked them for their hospitality and bowed appreciatively.

"Be careful, young man," the innkeeper said, bowing in return. "At the end of the pass is a village quite unlike any other. There are great dangers lurking in the shadows there."

I hesitated, looking deeply at the innkeeper, sensing the truth in his statement. I nodded uneasily. "Thank you for your warning," I said.

Thither walked me outside, to the end of the street, where the pass through the mountains began. He looked straight ahead, following the trail with his eyes. He patted me on the arm. "Don't forget to tell the great sorcerer that another apprentice is on the way."

I laughed. "I won't," I said, anxiously shifting the pack on my back. "Enjoy your stay." I waved at Thither and then turned and set off along the pass. I was aware that Thither looked after me, but I did not look back. I wanted to reach the village of Yarlung-Kyorpo before nightfall.

I was surprised to find that the distance to Yarlung-Kyorpo was very short. By noon, the village came into sight, a village that appeared no different from any other.

The trail ended where the village marketplace began. I paused, brushing the dust from my clothes and smoothing my hair with my hands, then I straightened myself and went up to a vegetable stall where a woman sat spinning a prayer wheel. She stopped spinning as I approached, greeting me as a potential customer.

I bowed politely. "I am seeking the Lama Yungtun-Trogyal," I said. "Can you tell me where to find him?"

The woman's face lost its expression. She began to spin her prayer wheel again. Instead of speaking her reply, she pointed down the street with her other hand.

I headed down the street, past the many vegetable stalls. Occasionally, a vendor would call out to me, asking me to buy his wares, but for the most part, I went unnoticed. When I had gotten out of the marketplace, I saw that there were many rows of houses, and far to the right on a hill was a many-storied structure made out of rock, surrounded by a high wall. I looked about for someone to ask and then saw a child hitting a stone up the street with a stick. I called out to the boy.

The boy stopped, turned, and looked at me.

I waved him near, smiling.

The boy looked around to make sure that it was he who was being called and not someone else and then picked up his stone and came over to me.

"You live around here?" I asked.

The boy nodded.

"Perhaps you know where the Lama Yungtun-Trogyal resides." I said gently.

The boy's eyes widened. He nodded.

"Would you tell me where?" I asked. "I am here from a village far away. I must find the Lama." It appeared that the boy would run off before answering but I quickly caught him by the arm. The boy stuttered and lowered his eyes. Turning around, he pointed to the structure on the hill opposite us.

I released the boy's arm and was about to thank him when he ran off. I looked after him, recalling how the woman in the marketplace began spinning her prayer wheel at the mention of the Lama's name. I shuddered, considering the task my mother had set before me. I was to submit myself to the Lama, to offer my possessions and my life in exchange for the sorcerer's power. I wondered if, in learning the secrets of evil and attaining its power, I would become like the sorcerer? If I would become feared as well? I hesitated, gazing up at the stone buildings on the hill.

CHAPTER FOUR
TWO-HEADED SERPENT CHAMBER

I rang the bell outside the monastery gate and waited, torn between running and staying, dreading the approach of the one who would answer it. The gate was solid wood flanked by stone pillars, and since I could not see if someone was coming, I listened. After awhile, not hearing anything, I bravely reached up and pulled the bell cord again.

A moment later, the gate swung open and a tall, powerfully built man dressed in black met my gaze. He did not speak, as if waiting for me to state my business.

"I am Milarepa from the village of Nyang, seeking the Lama Yungtun-Trogyal," I said uneasily.

"For what purpose?" the man in black asked.

"To become his apprentice," I answered.

The man in black eyed me suspiciously. "By whose recommendation?" he asked.

I hesitated, surprised and unsure of how to answer.

"You must come by recommendation," the man in black said again. His face was expressionless.

I still hesitated. I did not want to say that my mother had insisted, but it was the truth and I could think of nothing else." I am here at my mother's request and her demand that I learn the sorcerer's art so that I may avenge my family." I stopped, not wishing to tell the man more.

The man glared at me. His eyes seemed to reach out and hold me in place, examining me as I stood there. Suddenly, the man stepped back from the entrance and motioned to me to enter and follow him.

The monastery grounds were very plain. The earth was covered with a thin layer of pebbles, like miniature cobblestones, only they were loose and uncomfortable underfoot. An occasional blade of grass or sprig of weed grew in between and around them. In the center of the grounds was a large pool of water. Around it were stone benches. Grey-and-black-robed figures sat on them. Each seemed to be sitting alone and it was quiet, except for the occasional sound of a pebble splashing lightly as it was thrown into the water. No one bothered to look up as we passed.

On both sides of the monastery doors were shrines and in them were figures of serpents wrapped around the form of a man. I would have paused to study the sculptures but the man leading me had already ascended the stairs. He pushed the heavy door inward, waiting for me.

I hurried through the doorway, catching only a glimpse of the decorative details on the walls, before the door closed and the room fell into semi-darkness. The man quickly led me into the next room, which was well-lit by two large windows. "Wait here," the man said, raising a hand for me to stay. Without turning to check on me, he went through another doorway and into the next room, closing the door behind him. I heard voices but I could not make out what they were saying.

I looked around. The walls were decorated with colorful images of serpents. The predominant colors were red and green, but there was also a purplish color, all of which were painted or etched onto a solid black surface. The effect was stunning, pictures that brought to life a life-like illusion of the passions of man. In one scene a man was gorging himself on serpents; in another, a man stood high on a hill, using a serpent as a rod of power, striking its force to the skies to bring about a rain of hailstones. I stared at the scene, trying to understand the meaning of what I saw, recalling my mother's specific orders to acquire the knowledge of hailstorms to destroy my aunt and uncle's crops. I wondered if it was the serpents themselves that had the power. I saw what appeared to be proof of it in the next scene, which showed a man stabbing another man with the serpent-like rod.

The door opened. I quickly shifted my eyes to meet the gaze of the man in black who had brought me here. His expression was cold and unfeeling. "The Lama Yungtun-Trogyal has assigned you temporary quarters in the novice hall," the man said. "What have you to pay?"

I hesitated. I had expected to meet the Lama in person, to hand over all of my possessions to him. I was not sure if I wished to give this man anything. Reluctantly, I fumbled into the pocket of the grey cotton clothes given me by the innkeeper and felt the two gold coins. I withdrew one of them and gave it to the man in black.

The man took the coin and, without looking at it, put it in his pocket. He turned away. "You may follow me," he said.

I regretted having given the man one of my gold pieces. If I had had a lesser coin, a tin or copper, I would not have minded. But now I had given half of the Lama's money to someone else. I followed the man down the long, semi-dark hallway and into another corridor in another section of the great monastery. Indeed, we had walked so far and made so many turns that I was unsure if I could find my way out again. Finally, the man stopped in front of a closed door. It was marked with a double-headed serpent carved into the face of it. He turned to me.

"You are to stay inside until the Lama sends for you," the man said. "Everything you need is there and food will be brought to you." He turned and left me.

I looked after the man, watching to see which turn in the corridor he took but I was suddenly distracted by a noise from inside the room. I turned to face the door again. The double-headed serpent glared back at me. I listened uneasily, believing I had heard voices inside. Cautiously, I pushed the door inward.

The room was dark and empty. I stood in the doorway, looking in, not wanting to enter. If I allowed the door to shut behind me, I would be in total darkness. Using my body as a stop to hold the door, I carefully looked around. I saw from the faint glow of light in the hallway that the room was empty, that there were no windows in the room, nor was there any furniture except for a fleece spread out on the floor for sleeping. Seeing it, I sensed that I might be expected to remain in there for some time. Next to the fleece was a jug, which I believed contained tea or water, and I could see that there was an opening on the far wall for urinating. It was too dark behind the door to see how wide the room was or to see if there was anything hidden there. I hesitated, remembering how I had felt at the gate, unsure if I should enter or run. I tried to reason with myself, to rationalize that surely I could find my way out of the place if the need arose. Then I had an idea.

If I could reach the fleece, I could drag it forward, into the doorway, to keep the door from closing. I quickly studied the distance between where I stood and the fleece and, holding the door with one hand, I tried to reach it. My reach was an arm's-length short. I tried another way. Sitting on the floor with my back holding the door, I stretched out my legs. My toes touched the fleece, but I still couldn't quite reach it. To get more stretch, I lay down on the floor, using my head to hold the door. My feet gripped the fleece and dragged it to me, then I rolled it and shoved the bulge between the doorway and the door in such a way that the door remained fully open. Then I entered, using the faint light from the hallway to see my way around.

There was nothing there. I wondered why I had been brought to such a place. Had the man in black merely wanted my money? I recalled that the man had said that someone would come with food. I decided to sit in the open doorway on the fleece and wait. I would question whoever came. Sitting on the fleece, I looked down the narrow hallway, my back to the inside of the room.

Sitting there, I began to fear that I had not been accepted. My mother had sent me on a mission, and now that I had arrived at the place where I was supposed to be, I sat hidden in a corridor. Either the Lama had refused to see me and the man in black had stolen my money or I had been deceived. I considered that I could be deceiving myself.

How could I be deceiving myself? In what way? I had completed a grueling journey through the Himalayan mountains to this place where no one wanted to be.

Suddenly, it struck me. If no one wanted to be in the village of Yarlung-Kyorpo because of the terrible Lama, then why did so many live here? I thought of the woman in the marketplace and also of the child who had reluctantly directed me. Were the people forced into staying? I had seen no army or police to restrain them. The thin, dark, deep hallway brought to mind my mother's frequent comments about the Lama's great power. I shuddered. Could it be that the Lama's power forced the villagers to remain?

Sounds of laughter came from behind me. Startled, I quickly turned around, accidentally pushing the fleece outside the doorway and myself into the room. The door swung shut behind me before I could grab it. The fleece had been pushed outside. I backed up to the door, fumbling for a handle or a way to reopen it but could find none. My heart pounded, throbbing in my chest. It seemed so loud that, for a moment, I could not hear anything above it. If the laughter was still there, I could not hear it.

Standing with my back to the door, I gradually quieted myself. I remembered my beloved Zesay once telling me that the holy man Lama Kataka had explained that a man had nothing to fear but his own fear. At the time, the statement had meant little to me but now, feeling consumed by fear, I knew that it must be true. As my heartbeat softened, I recalled the layout of the room, that there had been nothing there, not even a window. I also remembered that I had not looked behind the door and I did not know if anything was there or not. Again, I moved my hands over the door, searching for a way to open it, but again I could find nothing. There was no way out, it seemed. Until someone opened the door from the other side, I would have to wait. They would come. Bending my knees, I squatted to the floor and sat with my back against the door so that no one could enter without my knowledge. When they did push the door open, I would grab it and get out. Looking into the darkness, I carefully listened for the laughter that I had heard earlier but I heard nothing. I wondered if someone lived on the other side of the opposite wall and had been in the room, laughing, and then had left again. I considered going to the wall and putting my ear to it but instead cautioned myself not to leave the door. If it should suddenly open, I wanted to be there, ready to grab it. I didn't want someone to shove food inside and run, leaving me a prisoner.

Hours passed and I was growing cold and miserable, sitting on the hard stone floor. I wished that the fleece was not on the other side of the door. I remembered the robe that my mother had made me and I withdrew it from my pack. I slipped my arms through the sleeves and retied the heavy cord around my waist again to hold it in place. At the same time, I checked the pocket to make sure the turquoise was still there, then I reached back into my pack for a piece of dried rat meat and ate. When I had finished, I was thirsty and remembered that there was a jug across the room but I decided that, since I was not sure what it contained, if anything, I wouldn't risk leaving my post by the door.

More time passed and I slipped into a light sleep. In that state, between wakefulness and sleep, I dreamed that an invisible messenger had come to fetch me. I was led back down the long corridors, past the place of murals where I had been, and into the black magician's private quarters. There I waited to meet the Lama Yungtun-Trogyal when suddenly, someone came up behind me and struck a heavy hand on my back.

The shock awakened me. I quickly looked about the darkness. Although I realized that I had been dreaming, I had the feeling that I had missed my meeting with the Lama, that someone had deliberately distracted me. A sudden, irresistible anger grew in me, and I was both astounded by my feeling and satisfied by it. If I had had something to smash at that moment, I would have done so, and in my rage, I thought of my evil aunt and uncle and how they had tormented my family, had robbed my mother of her youthful luster, and had suppressed Peta's future and my own. I hated them and, in that moment of silent rage, I saw an image of my aunt and uncle before me. I grabbed at them, tearing their arms and legs from their bodies, as though I was tearing branches from a tree, finally tossing their dismembered torsos aside. Looking up, I saw my mother smiling.

The scene gave way to another. Zesay was cradled in my arms, kissing me. I was overcome with passion. My penis swelled and throbbed until I could no longer endure it. I grabbed her skirts and ripped them aside. She tried to push me away but I held her to me, forcing my way between her legs, finally bursting inside of her.

I gasped and drew myself up on my knees, leaning heavily against the thick wooden door. Zesay had seemed so real. My behavior sickened me. To have violated her in that way would have violated our love and sacred trust. I would have scarred her as a woman, offended her and, in so doing, offended myself. I was ashamed, and yet I could not forget the feeling of pleasure. Touching myself, I realized that my body fluids had released and squirted all over my robes. Then I remembered what I had done to my aunt and uncle as well. I buried my face in my hands. Again, I could see my mother's face and again she was smiling. I tried to refocus my thoughts, to shift my attention in some other direction. An image of Thither came to mind, only it wasn't an image of friendship but of my suppressed jealous feelings toward him. I saw him as a threat, wishing that he would not follow me here, that he would turn around and go to Nar where he wanted to go in the first place. I didn't really want him here with his do-good ideas. Again, I caught myself. There seemed to be nothing but darkness flowing through me, taking form in anger, lust, and jealousy. I rubbed my eyes. What was happening to me? Was my mind degenerating in the serpent chamber prison?

I tried to reason the length of time I had been in the room but time seemed to mesh together, as though I had been both asleep and awake, and I remembered a similar feeling at the inn in Tsang, that of being unsure of how long Thither and I had slept. The feeling was the same, only at the inn there had at least been a window to finally determine the time of day. Also, I had not been alone.

Where was Thither now? Was he still in Tsang or had he left to join me? I envied Thither's easy manner, his slow, sure pace. His family had money and they had treated him like a nobleman, giving him everything money could buy, as well as offering their loving support for whatever he wished in life. Thither was visiting the black magician merely to learn what he could of the evil arts without becoming involved in them. I did not have that luxury and, although I considered Thither my good friend, I hated him for it.

I rested my head against the door and closed my eyes, telling myself in a low voice that I must relax and clear the ugly thoughts from my mind. Beneath my closed eyelids, images began to form again. I saw a shadow of myself in a dark pit and crawling over me was a two-headed snake. The serpent wound around me, inhaling my limbs with one head and exhaling them with another. It was an intense feeling, both painful and pleasurable, agony and ecstasy, full and empty, and between each feeling there was a lull, a moment of suspension whereby I touched some true part of myself, as though the primitive feeling that rushed through me was a part of my true nature.

The true nature that I became aware of was an entity within myself, an entity whose feelings were balanced and calm. Between the intense highs and the lows, I came to recognize this entity as the part of myself that was liked and respected, only this part would appear and disappear, like the wind on an autumn day. The balanced part of myself offered a feeling of ease and relaxation, but as soon as I tried to grasp it, it was swept away by painful memories, followed by those of lust and the desire for fulfillment, before gradually returning to balance once more. It was like folds in a cloth, one overlapping another. I came to realize that the balance existed because of the lows and the highs in feeling, that it was somehow stationed in between them. I contemplated the meaning. After some moments of struggling with the idea, it was as though a lamp had been lit, filling the room with light. I saw that both heads of the two-headed snake were resting upon my chest, smiling at me.

My body bumped forward as the door moved. I awoke suddenly to realize that someone was trying to enter the room. Quickly, I jumped to my feet, ready to grab the door when it opened.

The door opened and a flood of light entered the room. I squinted my eyes, momentarily blinded, and then gradually I looked into the firm but kindly face of an older man. The man held the door for me and motioned that I come outside.

I stepped to the other side of the door with my small pack of belongings. I was not in a long corridor as I had remembered, but in an exterior walkway. The day was bright and sunny. I considered that I might still be asleep, that the daylight was part of a dream, just as the kindly expression on the older man's face was also part of a dream.

"I am told you wish to see the Lama Yungtun-Trogyal," the older man said.

I turned to face him, still uncertain if I was awake or asleep. "Yes," I answered, looking into the brilliantly lit face. "My name is Milarepa. I am from the village of Nyang. I seek instruction from the Lama Yungtun-Trogyal, the mightiest of all black magicians."

The older man smiled but, as the glow of sunshine drifted

from his face, I saw shadow reflected in it. "To what purpose?" he asked.

A part of me sensed that I was dreaming, although I knew that it could not be so. "To avenge my family from the thieves who have stolen our fortune and treated us with unbearable cruelty. Only the Lama Yungtun-Trogyal has the power to teach me what I need to learn."

The form of the man opposite me suddenly changed and, for a moment, he appeared transformed into a snake. I felt my skin ripple and a cold chill raced up my spine. It was as if suddenly I knew who the man was. I sank to my knees and bowed low before the Lama and, reaching into my pocket, I withdrew the turquoise and the final piece of gold that my mother had given me. I handed them to the Lama with my head bowed. "I offer all that I have to you, my possessions and my life." I took off the robe my mother had made me and handed it, too, to the Lama. When I looked up again, the Lama was gazing at me.

"There are many who come to me," the Lama said, "but only a very few succeed. There are many who would achieve power only to misuse it. There are many unworthy ones who seek me for power."

"I wish only to accomplish my mission," I said, looking up, concerned that the Lama was misunderstanding me. Gazing past him, I could now see why I had thought that there had been a long dark corridor outside the room. The shadows and light played tricks under the eves of the monastery. "When my mission is accomplished," I said sincerely, "I will forget all that I learn from you. In that way, I can pose no threat to anyone."

The Lama motioned to me to rise. "One never forgets a true teaching," the Lama said. "If you learn enough to be successful, what you have learned will be with you always. Do you know what that means?"

I wanted to lower my eyes but I felt held by the Lama's gaze. I was both thrilled and frightened, and I knew that in another moment I would be accepted by the Lama, that a part of me would merge with him. As I stood locked into the Lama's gaze, the face of the black magician seemed to change, to darken more and more, until gradually I couldn't see him anymore. Somewhere in the distance, I heard him repeat the question he had posed to me. "Do you know what that means?"

Before I could grasp it, a loud rapping sound from behind startled me. I would have spun on my heels but I found that I was sitting and not standing, my back resting against the door. There was another rap against it.

"Are you in there?" a man's deep voice called. "I cannot open the door." I was too astonished to answer, realizing that I was still within the dark chamber where the man in black had left me. My meeting with the Lama had also been a dream. I rose to my feet and stood back. The door opened.

The dimly lit corridor that I had remembered stretched out behind a youthful man in grey robes. He carried a tray of food in his hands. Seeing the confused look on my face, he grinned, then looked down at the fleece at his feet, lifting it with one foot to draw notice to it. "You're a strange one, aren't you?" the young man said sarcastically. "You'd rather sit on the cold rock floor than the fleece, I see." I shook my head, still too uncertain to speak.

He pushed me with his elbow and moved past me into the chamber, leaving me standing in the doorway, and put the tray of food on the floor. He then went to the far corner of the room and picked up what I had believed to be a jug and, lifting the cover of it, struck a flint against the wall and lit the wick.

I watched. The jug was not a jug as I had believed, but a lamp. Immediately, the chamber took on a soft glow. Astounded, I looked about the room, seeing that the fleece was back inside and that the door remained open without anything holding it. I went to it. Looking up, I saw that a stick near the hinge held the door open. I turned to the young man who was no older than myself. "I didn't see you prop the door open," I said, eyeing him suspiciously. The young man stared at me and then went to the door, pushing it inward a bit further until the stick at the top snapped free and the door closed. I rushed to it, trying to grab it before it completely shut. The young man pushed my hands away. I stared at the closed door. A feeling of panic gripped me when the young man reached to the top of the door and pushed a lever. The door swung inward again. When it opened to a certain point, the stick clicked into place, holding it open. I turned to the young man and stared wide-eyed at him. "You mean, I was not locked in here?" I asked.

The young man smiled and shook his head. "Of course not,"

he said. "Have you never seen a door like this one, or a lamp?" He motioned to the light on the floor.

I shook my head. In my village there were no such doors, and in Nyang, a jug looked like a jug and a lamp looked like a lamp.

"Let that be a lesson," the young man said.

I was uncertain what he meant. "In what way?" I asked.

The young man smiled again, apparently amused by my ignorance. "Things are not always what they seem," he said, "especially here."

I recalled the many incidents that had happened while I believed myself locked in the chamber, including my meeting with the Lama Yungtun-Trogyal.

"I can see by your expression that you know what I am speaking about," the young man said. "But then that is the purpose of the two-headed serpent chamber." He hesitated, enjoying the amazement on my face before he continued. "Even if you had used the lamp and had been able to open the door, your experiences would have been the same, only you would not have feared them."

I stared at the young man. "You mean there is a power in this room?" I asked.

The young man nodded. "It is charged with power. Yes!" he said, searching my face.

I sensed he chose his words carefully, not wanting to say too much. "Have you ever been left in here?" I asked.

The young man nodded. His expression was thoughtful and sober. "When one first arrives at the monastery, one is brought here to meet the power. I was left here when I first arrived but now I am an acolyte. Before I am to become a novice, I will be brought here again."

I had many questions about the power of the room but did not want to miss the opportunity to learn what I could of the young man and his experience. I quickly asked, "How long have you been an acolyte?"

"Two years," the young man said, staring steadily at me. "And when will you be a novice?" I asked.

"When I am ready," the young man answered coolly.

I hesitated. I could feel that my questions were not welcome. "My name is Milarepa," I offered. "I am from across the mountain, from the small village of Nyang." I bowed in introduction.

"And I am Narquin," the young man answered, bowing slightly. "I must go now."

I was anxious. "How long am I to be left here, Narquin?" I asked.

Narquin had started for the door but now paused and turned to face me. "That is not for me to say," he said politely, eyeing me.

"Who is it that will say?" I asked.

"The Lama Yungtun-Trogyal," Narquin said. "He decides on everything." He paused and then added, "But the door is always open should you choose to leave on your own."

I lowered my head, shaking it from side to side, then I stretched out my arms to either side as if to dismiss the idea. Straightening again, I said, "Narquin, a friend of mine named Thither is to meet me here. If you see him, will you please tell him that I am well."

Narquin nodded. "If I see him," he said. Then he opened the door and went out, closing it behind him.

I followed after him, checking the latch on the upper right hand corner of the door, content that I could open it if I should choose to do so.

The lamp let off a thick musty odor, like that of a freshly killed animal, and I considered extinguishing it in order to clear the air. Gradually, however, I became accustomed to it and I decided that I would rather smell the thick scent of an animal's death than sit in darkness while I waited for the Lama to decide my fate. Over and over again, I recalled my meeting with the Lama, or at least what I believed to be my meeting with the Lama. I went over every detail in my mind again and again. It seemed that the Lama had been unimpressed by my gifts. I wondered if he had truly understood that I had given him everything that I had. Did the subtle change in expression on the Lama's face mean that it wasn't enough? What else could I have given him?

I remembered with some wonder that the Lama was not a terrifying man. He was not ugly as one would imagine the great black sorcerer to be. The lines of his face were firm and strong, and yet I distinctly recalled that I had seen the Lama's face as attractive. I quickly reminded myself that what I had seen could very well have been an hallucination or a dream. I had no way of knowing if I had truly met the Lama Yungtun-Trogyal, or did I?

I remembered the turquoise and the gold coin I had given the Lama, and quickly I fumbled about in my robe pocket trying to find them. At first, I believed them to be gone, but then I found them and drew them from my pocket. Holding my hand out in front of me, I stared at them, uncertain if the experience had been real or not.

Although it seemed that my experience had been a mystical one, I had never had any similar experiences with which to compare it. Zesay had frequently spoken to me of hers, however. It was not unusual for Zesay to have a premonition of a coming event, or even to know all about a person before she had met him. I hadn't believed her at first but she constantly proved it to me. After awhile I came to trust her inner vision and I recognized that she was special because of it. Was I now special as well?

Narquin had said that the two-headed serpent chamber was charged with a power. Did he mean that someone had charged the room with power? Was the purpose of that power to give visions to the one staying within it? If the visions were real, and they seemed to be, then to what purpose?

I was aware that my thoughts were racing in circles, questions asking questions, until gradually I grew tired of them. It was as though my mind was a separate entity, chattering away by itself. Bored, I no longer prodded for understanding and slipped into a light sleep instead.

This time, I knew I was dreaming. I remembered lying down on the fleece and slipping away from the noise in my chattering mind. When the door opened suddenly and Narquin entered again, I was not surprised because I knew that the door did not really open and Narquin had entered only in my dream.

"I see you did not eat your dinner," Narquin said, standing over me, looking down at the untouched tray of food.

I had forgotten all about it, yet I suddenly realized I was very hungry. I sat up with a start, fully awake, and began to eat. Narquin was not there.

The tray contained a variety of foods. There were root vegetables similar to those I had had with Thither in Tsang and a bowl of spicy stew. I couldn't identify many of the flavors, but they tasted good and satisfied the hunger I had felt. When I finished, I lay back down again.

Again, I was aware of myself drifting into sleep. It was as though I was watching myself do it. The idea amused me and, for a moment, I thought of Zesay and how I would have enjoyed sharing the experience with her but I quickly dismissed her from my mind. I knew that if I continued to think of her, my body would react sensually and I didn't want it to happen. Instead, I thought of Narquin and wondered what it was like to be an acolyte in the Lama's monastery.

And then it happened again. As though in a dream, I saw myself sitting on a bench around the lake in the monastery courtyard. Across from me, on another bench, was Narquin. He threw a pebble into the lake, watching as the stone broke the surface of the water, sending scores of circles spiraling outward. After a few minutes, he looked up and called over to me, motioning me near.

I rose from my seat, hurried over, and sat on the bench next to him. It was then I realized that it wasn't Narquin I sat next to, but rather, the Lama Yungtun-Trogyal. The Lama showed no reaction to my surprise, but pointed to the lake. "When the stone was thrown into the lake, what happened?" he asked.

I hesitated, unsettled by the change from Narquin to the Lama.

"When the stone was thrown into the lake, what happened?" the Lama asked again.

"It disturbed the surface," I answered quickly.

The Lama smiled. "Good," he said, nodding. "And where does the responsibility for the disturbance belong?"

I hesitated again. I wanted to say that the responsibility belonged to Narquin for throwing the stone into the water, but Narquin was not there. "To the one who threw the stone," I answered finally.

"That is correct," the Lama answered. "The stone is not responsible for the disturbance as many would believe. The stone is only an instrument to create the disturbance. It is the same with you, young man. Power itself is not responsible for disturbances.

Power is an instrument. The person who uses the power bears responsibility for its use." The Lama turned to me. "You do understand, don't you?"

I nodded. I did understand. While Zesay had never used power as an example to me, she did teach me many things that the holy man Lama Kataka had taught her. Yet, how could it be that a holy man's teachings and a sorcerer's teachings would be the same?

"They are both the same and yet not the same," Lama Yungtun-Trogyal said, answering my thought. "But that lesson is for another time. For now, I want you to become aware of the taste of power." I turned my head, looking into the water. When next I turned to him again, it was not the Lama who faced me, but Narquin.

I was so startled that I jumped to my feet.

Narquin looked up at me, laughing.

I opened my eyes. Although I was aware of lying alone in the two-headed serpent chamber, I could still hear Narquin laughing at me.

I rose to my feet and walked slowly around my cell. Now that I knew I could open the door and leave at any time, I no longer felt confined. Instead, I felt a compulsion to understand why it was that I was still in there, why I was experiencing what it was I was experiencing. I was there, I supposed, because I had not yet experienced something that I should experience.

I recalled how the great sorcerer had appeared in place of Narquin by the courtyard pool and how I had said that I was interested in having the experience of power. Was the great Lama referring to the power of the two-headed serpent chamber? I paused, looking about the room. When first I had entered, I believed the room to be larger, deeper that I now knew it to be. I had perceived the darkness as depth. The glow of the oil lamp dispelled that myth. The room was small, square-shaped, with only the door as an opening. Since Narquin had lit the lamp and showed me how to work the door, I was without fear and yet I had many strange experiences while there. Where was it to end? When would it end?

As though trying to find an answer, I walked to the door and put my hand on it, stretching my fingers over the rough surface. In my village there had been no such doors. Because of the shortage of wood, doors in Nyang were bamboo frames covered with cloth or skins. In the very poorest of homes such as mine, rice was pounded and mashed into thin sheets and then dried in the sun. This rice paper was then carefully stretched over the bamboo frame to seal out the cool night air. In the stormy season, however, this method was unsatisfactory. I could remember a childhood night, huddled with my sister Peta, after the rains and wind had ripped through the door our mother had made from rice. We had been chilled to the bone, and along with our mother, had taken ill. Zesay's parents had found us the next day and provided a more suitable door cover and then nursed our family back to health. I could still see Zesay's father, standing authoritatively with his hands on his hips, surveying the state of my family's home. The patriarch shook his head, saying. "My daughter's betrothed must be raised in stature or else he will be her doom."

The memory still made me angry. It was not Zesay's father's fault that he wanted someone of greater stature for his daughter. The betrothal had been made at a time when I was accepted as of noble birth. Sick and freezing in that room, I was a penniless nobleman. I was still a penniless nobleman. A sudden pain showed me that, in my silent anger, I was mashing my hand against the heavy wooden door and I quickly withdrew it. The flesh on my palm was slightly torn and I rubbed it for a moment, trying to ease the feeling, realizing, at the same time, that I was trying to erase the helpless feeling I had had as a child. I reached to the latch at the top of the door and stepped back, allowing the heavy door to slowly swing inward. When it clicked into place, in full open position, I went to the center of the doorway and looked down the long corridor. I wished that I could see someone, anyone. I was tired of being alone, of enduring the silent internal struggle with my memories, and I was also anxious to learn the secret of power from the great Lama Yungtun-Trogyal.

As I stood there, seeing no one, I remembered again how the Lama Yungtun-Trogyal had appeared in place of Narquin in my dream of the monastery lake. I wondered if the dream was really a dream or if it was a vision, or if there was any difference between the two. "Perhaps a dream and a vision are the same thing," I murmured to myself. "Perhaps I am dreaming or having a vision now." I recalled the pain of my hand as I mashed it on the door and decided that dreams or visions could not create physical pain. Turning around, I re-entered my cell and shut the door.

It was as if, by shutting the door, I had transported myself. I was no longer in the two-headed serpent chamber, but in the kitchen, watching grey-robed monks making tsamba for the evening meal. They didn't seem to notice me. One emptied bags of barley grain into a huge gourd, another added water, while still another mixed the ingredients with a long-handled wooden spoon. I watched. When the mixing was completed, the pastry dough was lifted from the vat and broken into little balls and rolled in yak butter. Then they were neatly stacked on a platter before an open fire pit. The pit, I knew, was to keep the dough warm so that it would rise to its fullest proportion before it was served. The rising also lightened the taste.

The monk who was rolling the tsamba into little round balls paused and seemed to look straight at me, although I felt sure he did not see me. "I understand the two-headed serpent chamber is occupied," he said lightly. He had a round face, thick lips, and deep-set eyes.

The other two monks kept working but looked at the other, waiting for him to continue.

"The new ones are such fun," the round-faced monk said again. "They don't take everything for granted."

"And most don't last very long either," the monk next to him said. "It is our assignment to keep the bellies of those who have come here to learn full."

"Oh, come now," the round-faced one said. "Is it necessary that we take everything so seriously?"

The monk who had not spoken looked up from his work. "What did you have in mind?" he asked.

"A little special dinner perhaps," the round-faced monk answered.

The other two stopped working and looked at him.

The round-faced monk grinned. His eyes were like deep, dark, sinister-looking slits in his head. He picked up a plate of the tsamba and carried it to the stone grinding table in the center of the kitchen and set it down. "If we had extra help in the kitchen, we could all have some time off," he said.

"The fellow you captured last time didn't last long," one monk said, watching him.

"Well, maybe this one will last longer," the round-faced monk said, still grinning. "It is worth a try, isn't it?"

The other monks nodded.

The round-faced monk punched a hole in each piece of tsamba and motioned to the other monks to join him at the stone table. They turned to one another. One shrugged his shoulders and the other laughed, then they went to where the round-faced monk waited.

The round-faced monk clapped his palms together in anticipation, then lifted a rolled tsamba to his lips and spit into the center of it. Before he put it down, he neatly closed the hole, looking to the other monks, watching as they followed his action. When they had finished, they turned to each other and grinned with satisfaction. The round-faced monk nodded approvingly, then drew back his robe, exposing his penis. Seeing this, the others did the same. All three then sprinkled the tsamba with their urine.

I was shocked at the scene and cried out in disgust and protest but went unnoticed by the monks.

The monks then neatly stacked the tsamba on a plate and decorated it with green onion tops. The round-faced one stood back and admired the plate of tsamba and then hurried to the pantry door and summoned an acolyte, handing him the plate of food, telling him to deliver it to the one in the two-headed serpent chamber. "When you return, you too may eat," the monk said cheerfully.

I protested, yelling at the monks, telling the messenger that the food was impure, but no one saw or heard me.

As the acolyte set out down the long corridor with the food, I hurried after him, chattering away about what I had seen, even though I knew the boy was not aware of my presence. The acolyte came to the door with the two-headed serpent carved on it and paused. I could sense a flurry of anxiety in him, as though he was remembering his own experiences in that room. Finally, the acolyte knocked at the door. He waited a moment and then pushed it open.

To my surprise, when the acolyte entered, I was already in the chamber waiting for him. Dumbfounded, I stared at the boy but could not speak. The acolyte too seemed at a loss for words. After a moment, he said, "The great Lama Yungtun-Trogyal sends you your meal." He handed the plate of food to me.

I looked at the plate and then at the messenger. I knew that I could not eat the disgusting food and yet, since it was given in the Lama's name, I knew I could not reject it either. "The Lama has been so generous with me," I said, hesitantly, "that I am no longer hungry." The acolyte looked at me curiously. "You are not hungry?" he asked.

Hunger pains clawed at my stomach. It had been many hours since I had eaten. "The ecstasy of being under the Lama's roof has filled my belly." I answered politely, bowing.

The acolyte stared at me and then looked quickly about the chamber, as if someone might be watching him. Satisfied that no one was there, he glanced hungrily at the tsamba. The old monk had promised him that when he returned from delivering the food that he too would be allowed to eat. If he returned the plate unemptied, the monks would no doubt be angry. They might give him nothing to eat at all. I knew it occurred to him that he could eat both what was meant for me and his own as well. Knowing my own appetite, I imagined that there was never enough food at the monastery and the prospect of a double portion would excite any healthy young man. The acolyte turned to me. "May I stay a few minutes and eat your meal?" he asked.

I withdrew my hands from the contaminated plate, giving the young man the food. I could not tell him what I had seen.

The acolyte stared at me anxiously, as though he was very hungry. I was hungry, too, but not for the disgusting plate of food. "Have you been at the monastery long?" I asked, changing the subject.

The acolyte became uneasy. "Not long," he answered, glancing from me to the plate of tsamba.

"I suppose you know Narquin?" I asked.

The acolyte was so surprised by the question that he nearly dropped the plate. He shook his head. "Where have you heard this name?" he asked, speaking softly.

"Why, from Narquin himself," I said. "He brought me food earlier." I paused, realizing the opportunity. The lie I was about to tell would sound so natural. "It is because of the huge portion of food that Narquin brought that I am not hungry."

The acolyte continued to stare. The name of Narquin had

visibly shaken him. "I know nothing except that which I am told," he said hesitantly.

It was now I who was surprised. Narquin had said that he was merely a servant in the Lama's monastery. Why then did this fellow seem so taken by his name?

The acolyte placed the food on the floor next to the fleece and turned to leave.

I watched the boy who was a few years younger than I. I didn't know his name but I could not forget the frightened look on his face, how his greed had been displaced by it. When the boy left, I went to the door and shut it and then looked down at the plate of food next to my bed, remembering with disgust how the kitchen monks had contaminated it with their body fluids. It was obvious that they believed they would entrap the one who ingested it. I shivered as a cold chill crept up my back. If I had not seen what the monks had done, I would have eaten the food.

How had I seen the monks?

I sat down and stared at the plate of tsamba, recalling the incident. I shut the door to my cell, turned around and suddenly found myself in the kitchen, watching the monks at their folly. I also remembered that prior to that I had been with Narquin, who had turned into the Lama Yungtun-Trogyal. The Lama had said that he wanted me to experience the power within the two-headed serpent chamber. Was it the power that transported me to the kitchen to see the plot against me?

The answer came as a slow rise within me. I thought of Zesay and her knowledge of things. I knew that she would explain the actions of the monks as works of sorcerers exercising black magic. She would point out to me that what I had experienced was the nature of the power I was to learn. At the monastery, I had been given a classic lesson in magic, although my mind could not accept it. I refused to believe that the monk's disgusting acts would have given them power over me if I had eaten the food.

I wondered how long I was to be left in the two-headed serpent chamber. I knew I could not stay much longer without nourishment and the next meal prepared by the monks might be as bad as the first.

I reached for my pack and searched through it for leftover food, but there was none. I had eaten the last bit some time ago. I also checked the pockets of the robe my mother had made me, feeling the turquoise and the gold coin, remembering how in a dream I had given it all to the Lama. I remembered, too, that the Lama had visited me in the serpent chamber and that he had already terminated my stay in that chamber but that, until now, I hadn't realized it. The revelation was clear. I gathered my belongings and rose to my feet, pausing to look quickly around the chamber, and then went to the door, opened it, and stepped outside.

CHAPTER FIVE
THE PAYMENT

The monastery courtyard was flooded with sunlight and, although there were many walking about, no one seemed to notice me. It was a peculiar feeling, as though I was invisible. I looked around, studying the faces of those nearest me, recognizing no one. I walked over to the lake in the center of the courtyard and gazed into it, seeing that I did indeed reflect on the mirror-like surface. Staring at the surface of the water, I gradually became aware that, even though I could see no other reflection in the water, there were others near me. An uneasy feeling crept over me and I turned to look at the robed figures once more. I believed myself to be dreaming again. Someone in the distance waved. I remained, standing motionless, looking between the heads of the grey-and-black-robed figures. The one who waved appeared and then disappeared again, hidden by heads and brilliant sunlight.

I began to move slowly toward the person, making my way invisibly through the throngs of monks, but the one who waved seemed not to be there. I turned and looked around again. There were monks walking singly, as well as sitting around the lake. There were others gathered about the shrines. If anyone talked to another, he was very quiet about it because there seemed to be total silence.

Not even a bird chirped. Standing there, it occurred to me that I had not left the two-headed serpent chamber after all, as I had believed, but had somehow slipped into a light sleep and was now dreaming that I was in the courtyard. I pinched myself, shook my head, and then laughed aloud, but, except for the sound of my own laughter, I still heard nothing.

It was a dream! I was dreaming of myself in the courtyard. I was not awake. I was sure of it, yet I distinctly recalled gathering my things from the two-headed serpent chamber and leaving it. The feeling was extremely odd. Where was I?

I tried to think. One moment I was leaving the two-headed serpent chamber and the next I was in the courtyard. I had no memory whatsoever of walking down the long, grey corridor or of discovering the courtyard. I left the chamber and the next moment I was here. I had not eaten the food the kitchen monks had prepared so it was not possible that my circumstances were brought about by the food.

Someone suddenly touched my shoulder from behind. The touch was shocking, sending me twirling about on my heels. I came face-to-face with Thither.

Thither smiled. "After following you on those mountain passes for so many weeks, I'd recognize the back of you any place," he said lightly.

I was too astounded to speak. If this was a dream then where had Thither come from? I stared at Thither disbelievingly, as though he were part of the hallucination. Gazing not only at him but around him, I saw that the courtyard had changed. The monks within it seemed more real. I could hear the monks talking among themselves, and in the background, birds were chirping.

"You look like you have seen your father's ghost," Thither said seriously. He was aware that I was greatly surprised by something. "It is kind of a dreary place, isn't it?" Thither looked around as if he were trying to think of something to say.

I nodded, glancing at my friend and then around the courtyard. Everything seemed quite normal, as though I had been mistaken about the dream. "When did you get here?" I asked.

"Just now. The gate was open and so I walked in." Thither paused, grinning. "The first person I saw was you, looking as though you were lost." Thither paused again, then asked, "Were you?"

"It felt that way," I said absently, remembering.

Thither hesitated, looked around, and then asked, "When did you get here?"

"The same day I left you in Tsang," I answered, uncertain how long ago that had been.

"A week today," Thither said.

I didn't answer but slowly gazed about the courtyard, trying to think of what day it was. "Many peculiar things have happened, and somehow the passage of time is lost among them," I said after a few moments.

"Have you met the Lama Yungtun-Trogyal?" Thither asked, allowing his eyes to wander about the courtyard as he did so.

I nodded, raising my forefinger to my lips. It was not a name to be spoken casually aloud.

"You have seen him?" Thither whispered, asking the question again.

"Yes," I answered. I looked directly at Thither, wanting to tell him how I had seen and met with the Lama, but uncertain and uncomfortable about doing so. Suddenly, I saw why. The monk in black, who had first greeted me at the monastery gate, was now coming up behind Thither. I motioned to Thither to turn around. "The gatekeeper is coming," I said.

Thither turned around as the man in black approached and bowed respectfully. Thither and I also bowed.

The gatekeeper waited for us to rise. He looked directly at Thither. "Are you here with an invitation?" he asked in a low voice. His expression was grave.

"He is the friend I mentioned who was to join me," I answered for him.

As though he did not hear me, he continued to stare at Thither, waiting for an answer.

"No," Thither said, "but I am here from a village near Nyang in a quest for knowledge. Lama Kataka sent me, saying that certain curiosities can be satisfied only by meeting the great Lama Yungtun-Trogyal."

"You are Kataka's student then?" the man in black asked.

I waited for my friend to answer, thinking of Kataka and how

Zesay loved and respected him. It seemed strange for a holy man to send his student to a black magician for knowledge.

"I was Kataka's student," Thither said. "It is now my mission to move on from him, to learn more. The Lama Kataka himself told me that there was nothing more he could teach me."

I turned from Thither to the gatekeeper, ready for my friend to be escorted inside as I had been, but was surprised when the man in black told him to wait near the lake. He would seek an answer on Thither's behalf and would return to give it to him.

I went with Thither, walking silently to the lake where we sat down on a vacant bench.

Thither turned to me. It was clear that he was uneasy and I felt the same way. "It certainly is a peculiar place, isn't it?" he said, grinning, and trying to make light of it.

I nodded but did not answer. There was so much to tell Thither and yet it seemed impossible to begin.

"Tsang was a fine experience," Thither said, changing the subject. "By the end of the week, I had become great friends with the innkeeper and his wife. Lovely people." He paused, studying the grim expression on my face. "And Tsang is such an exciting place. They have theatre—places where people act out stories from life. Have you ever been to a theatre?"

I shook my head, unable to concentrate on what he was saying.

"What's wrong with you?" Thither asked, concerned. "This place is creepy enough but you are making it worse."

"You stayed in Tsang a week?" I asked.

Thither stared at me. "It was what we agreed," he answered, sensing that something very odd had happened in his absence. "Wasn't that the agreement?" he asked.

I nodded.

"I was to finish out the week in Tsang and meet you here," Thither continued, as though defending himself. "Well, on schedule, here I am."

I drew my shoulders up to my neck and released them with a long sigh. "It means I have been here a week," I said again.

"Yes, I suppose that's true," Thither answered, watching me closely, as if listening for something that I had not said.

I took my time before speaking again. I sat for a long

moment looking into Thither's eyes, trying to choose the words to explain. "Since I have been here, I have not known if I was asleep or awake," I said, feeling the hollowness of my words as I spoke them. Because Thither showed no expression, I tried again. "Everything has a dreamlike quality to it around here and it leaves me feeling uncertain if I am asleep or awake. And if I do sleep, it feels like only a few hours. I know, since you are here, that that must not be true, that it has been a week as you say, but it doesn't feel that way. I could swear it has only been a few hours."

"Have you been drugged?" Thither asked.

I shook my head. "No," I answered, certain that I had not been. I had not eaten anything except the food from my own pack and I had nothing to drink. Yet, it had been a whole week. I must have had other food and drink as well. "To my knowledge, they have done nothing to me but leave me in a room by myself," I said. Then, I remembered the food Narquin had brought me, how I had awakened from a dream to ravish it. I told Thither about Narquin and the dream.

"I thought you said you met the Lama Yungtun-Trogyal?" Thither asked uncertainly.

"I did," I answered, "but while I was asleep." I told him one dream about the Lama chatting with me at the lake.

Thither tilted his head, studying me. "You are sure you were asleep?" he asked.

I nodded, recalling how Narquin had been talking with me and then changed into the image of the great Lama.

"And was he the great wrathful and victorious teacher of evil that his name implies?" Thither asked, mocking me.

I was jolted by his tone of voice and looked uneasily at the nearby monks before answering. "I don't know that," I answered quietly. "He was not unkind to me. I will say one thing. Although the meeting was brief, there was no doubt of the Lama's power."

"Did he say that he would teach you?" Thither wanted to know.

"Not directly."

I quickly looked around the courtyard. I first sensed that the man in black was coming and then I saw him. As we watched his approach, Thither whispered, "I must meet this Lama."

We rose from our seat and bowed to the man in black.

"The Lama Yungtun-Trogyal will see both of you now," the man in black said in an expressionless voice. "You will follow me." He turned and led the way. I followed behind Thither. We were entering the monastery through the heavy doors. I noted the shrines on both sides and saw that Thither noticed them as well. The sculptures were figures of serpents wrapped around the form of a man. Thither hesitated, trying to get more than a glimpse of them, and then hurried through the doorway, followed by me.

As the doors shut behind us, we were enveloped in darkness but, for an instant, I saw the same decorative details on the walls. As before, the man in black led us into the next room, which was well-lighted by two large windows. It was the mural room, which had fascinated me on my first visit there, only this time I had no time to look at it. The man in black ushered us quickly through it and into the next room.

A dark, rosey-pink glow filled the room and the air had a heavy musty scent to it. The room was small and without furniture, and the walls were clear of decoration, reflecting the pinkish color. The man in black bowed in the empty room, as though someone was present, and then he left me and Thither standing there.

We did not speak. I felt as if there was a sudden large lump in my chest. It was growing, tapping louder and louder as it grew, until it sounded like a thump. The sound of its thumping came from my heart and I could not control it. There was sudden, unbearable pain. I fell to my knees and grabbed my chest with my hands. Thither saw this and dropped to his knees trying to help me. For a moment, I thought I might die. Then, just as suddenly as it had come upon me, the pain let up. The pink glow in the room intensified, and at the center of it, there was a brilliant, pink, oblong globe of light. We raised our heads, looking at it, and watched as the oblong light darkened and took form. A young man appeared.

It was Narquin!

I looked up sharply, surprised to see him, and rose to my feet. Thither hesitated, then rose to his feet as well.

Narquin stood motionless and expressionless. I recalled his visit to the two-headed serpent chamber and how he had dispelled my illusions about being locked in the total darkness of it. He had shown me how to open the door and he'd shown me how to light the lamp. He had said to me that "things were not always as they seemed." I also recalled how, once in a dream, while sitting and talking with Narquin by the courtyard lake, his form changed into that of the Lama Yungtun-Trogyal. I also recalled the expression on the kitchen boy's face when I mentioned the name of Narquin to him. The boy had been unnerved by the mere mention of his name.

"Are you the Lama Yungtun-Trogyal?" I asked bravely.

Thither breathed heavily next to me, as if waiting for a reply.

Narquin bowed slightly and said, "The great Lama Yungtun-Trogyal has asked me to speak with you. He wished to know your motives for coming here." He looked first at Thither.

Thither stepped forward. "I seek the great one's knowledge so that my education may be completed. For years, I have studied with my village Lama and other Lamas who passed through our village. They told me that they could teach me nothing more, that if I wished to be a Lama myself, I must first look to the dark side of my nature for a deeper understanding of myself."

"Your goal then," Narquin repeated, "is to become a Lama."

"Of the highest order," Thither answered.

"Of evil or good?" Narquin asked, studying him.

"Neither," Thither answered. "It is my wish to move beyond good and evil into the higher orders."

Narquin stared at Thither for a long moment. Rays of rosey-colored light sparkled from him. "And what have you brought the Lama in return for his knowledge?" he asked.

Thither reached into his robe pocket and withdrew a handful of gold coins. He handed them to Narquin.

Narquin took the coins and nodded. "I shall see that the Lama receives them," he said, then he turned to face me.

I continued to look at him, thinking that he seemed taller than when we had first met. "I seek the Lama's knowledge to destroy those who have stolen my lands and fortune so that my widowed mother and my sister will be restored to their rightful places in the community," I said. Then I quickly reached into my robe pocket and withdrew the turquoise my mother had sent as a gift and the remaining gold coin. I then took off my robe and that, along with the turquoise and gold, I handed to Narquin. "I have nothing more," I said. "I have no other possessions."

Narquin accepted them. "You may both stay and learn what you will," he said in an even voice. "You will be provided with a room to share, food, and clothing. The escort who brought you here will guide you to your quarters. He waits for you in the next room." Narquin bowed, dismissing us, and remained in that position until we left the room.

We followed the man in black down a long, dark corridor, but not the same one I remembered. This one had many doors and from behind them came the occasional chatter of voices. We were in the monastery dormitory. The floors were rough stone like the streets outside, and the doors, unlike the wooden one of the two-headed serpent chamber, were made of familiar animal skins stretched over wooden frames. We had passed a number of such doorways when the man in black stopped, lifted a skin back from an opening, and told us to enter.

Thither stepped through the doorway first and I followed. The room was small and it had a dirt floor. There were three yak-skin fleeces, one against each of the three doorless walls, and next to each was a lamp and a small storage basket for our personal things. It was plain to see that someone already occupied the place on the left wall. Bits of clothing and writing instruments were left lying on that fleece. I turned to ask the man in black about the other person but he had gone.

"I saw him leave," Thither offered, seeing that I had expected the man in black to be there. "I don't suppose he would have been much help to us anyway." He slipped his pack from his back and stepped toward the yak fleece to the right of the door. "Do you mind if I take this one?" he asked.

I started to object, aware that my bed would then be in direct line with the door each time it opened, but it was too late. Thither had already gone behind the door and seated himself on the fleece.

"I wonder when we eat," Thither said, watching me as I looked around the room. "The room is better than I expected," he added. "I have heard that some monks have no comforts of any kind. I am so glad we do not have to sleep on the dirt."

I did not answer. As I went to the fleece directly ahead of me and slipped off my pack, I thought of the two-headed serpent chamber and wondered why I had been taken there at first instead of to the dormitory. For some reason, Thither was being given different treatment than I had been given. Why?

"How's the food at this place?" Thither asked again.

I turned and looked at him. It was true that Thither was a different sort than myself. Thither was more refined. It was obvious from his appearance that life had not challenged him in the same way it had challenged me. Thither had never suffered. How could I explain my vision of the kitchen monks tainting my food with their body fluids. I was not sure Thither would believe me, and if he did, I feared that he would decide to leave the monastery. I did not want to be left alone. "Have you any food left from Tsang?" I asked finally.

Thither shook his head. He had not brought extra provisions because he had not believed them to be necessary. He had taken it for granted that the monastery would feed him. "Don't you think we'll eat tonight?" he asked anxiously.

I looked away, trying to think of what to answer, when suddenly the door to our chamber opened. The boy acolyte, who had brought me the tainted food from the kitchen monks entered. I rose up on my knees in disbelief.

The boy stared back at me. His hand was still holding the door. He appeared to be uncertain, as if he had entered the wrong room.

"Who are you?" Thither called out, breaking the silence.

The acolyte looked at Thither, who was seated on the fleece next to mine. "I live here," he said quietly, turning his eyes from Thither to me again. "How is it you are here?" he asked.

"We were brought here by the gatekeeper," I said. "He told us we were to share this room with you."

"But how did you leave the...." The boy stopped himself, uneasily looking around the room.

I had the urge to jump to my feet and question the boy but something within cautioned me. I remembered how frightened he had been at the mention of Narquin's name. If he were pushed to explain himself now, he might rush off again. "My name is Milarepa and this is my friend Thither. We are both from the other side of the mountains, near Katmandu." I bowed respectfully, hoping my polite introduction would put him at ease.

Thither bowed as well.

"I am called Steita," the boy responded, bowing in return.

"Thither was just asking when next we eat," I said, looking up at the boy, who was still holding the door.

"Yes, I am very hungry," Thither added quickly.

"It is time now," Steita said. "I only returned to get my eating sticks." He paused, going over to his sleeping mat. Next to it was a small basket, which he opened, taking out two slim eating sticks. He turned around and showed them to us. "You should each find sticks in your baskets," he said. "You must have them in order to eat in the dining hall, and they are the only ones you will ever receive. The sticks," Steita said reverently, "are the Lama's gift to us. They are the tools of our nourishment."

I watched the boy as he spoke. It was obvious he worshipped the Lama and I noticed that when he mentioned him by name, he lowered his eyes. The boy seemed a bit simple-minded to be in training to become a black magician.

"Your sticks," the boy reminded, seeing that I was still looking at him.

Thither had his sticks in hand and had risen to his feet.

I reached for my sticks and rose as well.

The dining hall was long and narrow. Grass mats had been spread on the floor down the center and on both ends. A stone table was set at the entrance and it was here that each monk, novice, and acolyte, in that order, received a small basket filled with rice, meat, and a few root vegetables. Once the baskets were filled, each carried his food to a place in front of the grass mats and sat down.

I scanned the serving area, expecting to see the kitchen monks whom I had seen in my vision, but they were nowhere around. Relieved, I told myself that my vision had been merely a nightmare, a trick of the serpent chamber to frighten me. Perhaps that was why I had been brought there in the first place. Perhaps the Lama wanted to know how easily I could be tricked.

Thither filled the small bowl that was handed to him, adding to it as much as he could, and then waited for me and Steita. The smells of hot roasted meat tormented my rumbling stomach. With filled bowl, Steita moved ahead of us and led us to a place at the far end of the mat and sat down, motioning for us to sit quietly and wait. It was obvious from where we were seated that we had little position in the Lama's community.

My attention was caught by the lines of monks in black chubas and, for a moment, I saw the gatekeeper. It seemed as though the gatekeeper glanced at us as well and then quickly looked away. He was seated on the end of a cross row and next to him, to his left, were twelve other monks. They were all waiting patiently.

I turned and looked around. The mats were full. The center section, where we sat, was filled with those wearing grey robes, except for Thither and myself. It was obvious that we were the newcomers and yet no one paid us much attention. I noticed too that some of those in grey robes had matching grey ropes about their waists like Steita, while others had black ropes. I supposed that the grey was a sign of an acolyte and that black was the sign of the novice.

It was difficult to see the faces of those present. The hall was dimly lit, illuminated by yak-oil lamps situated on the grass mats at intervals of every thirteenth person. As the lights flickered, those seated nearest to the lamps took on eerie expressions.

The hall was very quiet when, suddenly, as though silently instructed to move on an invisible cue, all lifted their bowls and began to eat.

The food was pleasant but not filling. I could have eaten three times that amount, and from the glance Thither directed toward me as he lowered his empty bowl, I knew that he was still hungry as well. We waited quietly for everyone to finish, hoping for a second portion to be served, but it was not the case. Instead, Steita turned to us, motioned to us to keep our sticks and leave, following after him. Simultaneously, we rose to our feet and left the dining hall. Others in the hall were also leaving.

"It is nearly time for contemplation," Steita whispered as he moved ahead of us in the hall. "We must return to our rooms quickly. I must put my sticks away and then leave."

Thither and I glanced at each other. We wanted to question him but he moved ahead of us with quick steps, as if he were already late. I stared at the boy's back, listening to Thither grumble about being hungry as he walked behind me. I knew that Steita was hungry as well. "Is there nothing more, late at night perhaps, to eat in the kitchen?" I asked Steita softly.

Steita turned sharply and glared at me and then he turned away. We had arrived at our chamber. Steita quickly pushed the covering from the doorway. He went directly to the basket nearest his sleeping fleece and put his eating sticks into it. He then turned around, meaning to speak to us, but was caught by what he saw. I looked up while leaning over my sleeping fleece, lifting a grey chuba from it. I held it up in front of me and turned about to show it to Thither.

Steita bowed as I stood in front of him, holding the robe. When he rose again, he said, "You are accepted by the Lama. You have been given the robe of the acolyte."

I turned to Thither, who was looking at me.

Thither stuck out his lower lip, nodded, and then shrugged his shoulders. "There is not one for me," he said disappointedly.

'Yours will come," I said. I raised the robe and slipped it over my head and shoulders, adjusting it as it fell loosely about my lean body. Then I picked up the strand of grey rope that had been left with it and tied it around my waist. "How does it look?" I asked Thither, outstretching my arms from my side.

"Mysterious," Thither answered, trying to make light of it. It was obvious he wished that he had been left a robe as well.

"Now that you are an acolyte, you must come with me," Steita said.

I turned to face him.

"The monks have assembled already," Steita said urgently. We must hurry."

I straightened the robe nervously. I didn't know what the monastery contemplation would be like but I did know that, at last, I was beginning to tread the path to power, that I was beginning to fulfill my promise to my mother and I could not hide my feeling of hopefulness as I turned to face Thither.

Thither was sitting on his fleece, leaning against the wall, his legs stretched out in front of him. He appeared to have accepted the idea that he was not yet allowed to participate, until he saw my face. Then something odd stirred in his expression. I lowered my eyes, remembering how once Thither had seen me in a ray of sunlight, sitting beneath the tree in the forest early in our journey together. I wondered if Thither would have another sudden urge to bow down before me but I quickly dismissed the idea, feeling foolish for it.

"My opportunity is a different one at a different time," Thither said confidently. "I will catch up with you. Go about your mission now so that I can go about mine."

Contemplation was held in the dining hall, but in the brief time that it had taken us to return to our chambers, the hall had been transformed. The eating mats had been rolled up and stacked at the back of the hall. The floor, I could now see, was of smooth, dark-colored earth, treated by years of careful oiling to keep the texture clean and comfortable. In the center was a large, round, red silk cloth, and seated on the outside of the circle were the monks in their black chubas. There was a space and then another circle of monks, novices this time, encircling them and then again there was another circle, a circle of acolytes. It was in this last, outer circle that I sat with Steita. I watched as Steita carefully adjusted the folds of his robe about him and sat cross-legged, and I followed suit. When I had seated myself and settled in a somewhat comfortable position, I raised my head. The flickering yak-oil lamps brought to mind Thither's comment to me as I stood before him in my robe for the first time. Thither had said that I looked "mysterious," and mysterious was exactly how I would describe the appearance of the gathering in the great hall. Between the heads of the other acolytes, novices, and monks, I could see that the area that was covered by the red silk circle was still unoccupied. I wondered if the Lama would seat himself there but I also doubted it. If the Lama were to suddenly arrive, he would have to crawl over the tight circles of seated attendees. There had been no passage left through the circle of monks, making it impossible for anyone to enter.

Gutteral sounds of voices arose above the silence, moaning a lone chat in the great hall. It stopped. I looked at the inner circle and watched as those in black chubas raised long, tube-like trumpets, called yaklings, to their lips and blew. The sound rose above the silence and clapped against my ears. It was haunting and powerful in tone and, for an instant, I could not define it. A slow chill crept up my back and I pressed the palms of my hands over my ears to quiet the sound. When the sound of the trumpets faded, the moan of human voices rose again. This time I heard Steita's voice as well, and the ennunciation of what he said was AUM. Over and over again the sound of AUM was chanted, long and drawn out. The great hall was charged with it, filling it. I began to sing the strange song as well... AUMMMMMMM. I closed my eyes, listening a moment, and then sang the word and listened again. I had the distinct feeling that I was being consumed, merging with the force of the AUM, not merely by the sound but with the essence of it, and I began to relax, giving in, yielding, allowing my body to sway with the pulsating rhythm.

While singing the sound, I thought of my home in Nyang. It was as though I was actually standing outside of my mother's small, humble home; and looking into it, I saw her sitting on the dirt floor, her tired, rough hands fashioning some reeds into the shape of a basket. Her face was expressionless, as though the movements of her task had no meaning. No facial muscle moved nor did her eyelids flicker. Then, quite suddenly, she lifted her head and looked directly at me. She stared at me for a long moment, and from her look, I received a feeling that I had not felt since I left home. In the solemn gaze of my mother's eyes, I felt her anger and the hatred that she held for the injustice dealt her by life. It reached out to me like talons from a panther's paw. I jumped as though someone had touched my flesh with the point of a knife and lowered my eyes. When I lifted them again, it was not my mother I saw but the Lama Yungtun-Trogyal.

I stared at the Lama in disbelief. Was I dreaming? Was I dreaming I was dreaming? Had the image of my mother's hatred called the Lama to me?

The Lama's cold, hard stare continued the feeling that my flesh was being pricked by the cold metal edge of a knife. I stared back at the Lama, afraid to lower my eyes. There was no doubt that the man before me now was the same man who had entered my dreams in the two-headed serpent chamber. Yet the man was different. There was no manner of softness about him, as I had felt at the monastery lake. The Lama's gaze was now a demanding one, almost threatening me.

"Rise! Rise and step into the inner circle," the Lama commanded. The Lama's body seemed to enlarge, actually grow in size, as it rose above me, dwarfing me.

I swayed unsteadily, awed by the looming figure of the great Lama Yungtun-Trogyal, the victorious teacher of evil. The force of the Lama's presence was overwhelming. I could not help but obey his demand and, as though moving under the Lama's control, I rose to my feet and easily stepped between the other acolytes, the novices, and the inner circle of monks, stepping finally into the red silk circle. Then, as though responding to a further command, I sat down in the center.

The silence was intense. There was not a sound of movement or breath and, although I longed to gasp for air, my lungs seemed to refuse to function. I could not breathe at all. My heart throbbed in a struggle to maintain its beat. It seemed that it was growing, expanding to a size my chest could no longer contain and, at that instant, I again saw the great and powerful Lama Yungtun-Trogyal. The Lama stepped toward me with a gigantic outstretched hand and struck it into my chest. I doubled over in pain. His hand was like a screw, twisting into me like the turning of a skewer, clawing its way through my flesh. I was helpless. Then to my horror, a spurt of blood gushed from my chest and ran down my mid-section. The Lama twisted his hand in my chest again and let out a triumphant yell. I screamed in pain as I felt something rip free from inside my chest. For a moment, I remained breathless and then suddenly my breath returned. It was gradual at first. I wrapped my arms about my chest to ease the pain and noticed that the blood had stopped flowing, although it was smeared in thick patches all about the front of my new grey chuba. There was blood but there was no pain. Either I had died or the experience had been an illusion. Astonished, I looked up.

The Lama now stood directly above me. His hand was covered with blood and he held a heart in it, and the heart pulsated with life. "It is your heart," the Lama growled, holding it closer for me to see.

I was horrified and could not speak. It did indeed appear to be a human heart.

"You have asked to become a sorcerer," the Lama said. "Your heart is the price for the knowledge you seek. Now that you have paid the price, there is no turning back."

I was dumbfounded. The pulsating heart in the Lama's hand seemed somehow connected to me, as though I could feel it beating both in the Lama's hand and in my own chest as well. A cold chill continually rippled up my spine. I moved my hand over my chest to feel for the familiar beat.

The Lama smiled, watching me. He held the heart in front of his chest, over that place where his heart would be, then he moved his hand away. My heart remained suspended over his, as though attached. It was my heart that hung alive, exposed, pulsating on the Lama's chest.

I tried to deny what my senses told me, yet each time the heart beat on the Lama's chest, I could feel it. When I took a breath, I noticed that the Lama took a breath as well. My horror intensified as I noticed that when the Lama smiled, my own lips turned upward. When the Lama frowned, I frowned. It was as though my every movement and feeling was a mimick of the Lama's, as though by taking my heart, the Lama had taken my identity. I was no longer Milarepa, the orphaned son of a nobleman. I was attached to the Lama Yungtun-Trogyal. My heart beat next to the Lama's heart. Although I did not yet know the true meaning of my circumstances, I did know that I would never be the same. I was no longer the innocent boy from Nyang. I was controlled by a power that would eventually consume me. And, as I realized this, I closed my eyes. An image of my bleeding, pulsating heart followed me into the darkness. I tried to blot it out but my interior eyes refused, and in the darkness of my closed eyelids, I saw that a thin red thread connected me to the Lama.

"Milarepa, Milarepa," a voice whispered next to my ear. "Milarepa, we must leave now. Can you hear me?"

I opened my eyes to see Steita gently shaking my limp body, which sprawled before him on the floor. "You must get up, Milarepa," he said again.

I closed my eyes and opened them again. At first, I saw only darkness. Gradually, I became aware of Steita and began to regain control over my body.

"You must get up now, Milarepa" Steita urged. "It is late. All the others have gone."

I lifted my head. I was lying nowhere near where the circle of red silk had been. I was still where I had seated myself next to Steita, where we had sat together during contemplation. I touched my chest, leaving my hand there a moment until I could be sure of the beat within it, and then I sat up. "How is it I fell asleep?" I asked.

"You were not asleep," he said, watching me. "Whatever you remember has happened to you."

I gazed at the boy and then lowered my eyes, remembering and yet not wanting to remember. I was certain that it must have been a dream, yet I was also certain that I remembered the Lama ripping the heart from my chest. The pain had been excruciating. I remembered, too, that the Lama had said that he had taken my heart in payment for what I was about to learn. I lowered my eyes and lifted my head to see if the blood stains were still on my chuba. The front of my robe had a deep, dark spot on it. Nauseated, I dropped my head to the floor again.

"Did you think it wasn't true?" Steita asked, glaring down at me.

I wanted to question Steita but I was afraid.

"It is true," Steita said, answering the question I could not ask. "You have paid dearly for what you will receive." He grinned sadistically. "Now, get up. We must get out of here." He tugged at my arm but I still did not move. I could not believe that what I had dreamed was possible, unless, of course, I was dead. And if it was true that I was dead, I didn't care if I left the hall with Steita or not.

"I cannot wait for you any longer," Steita said impatiently. He tugged at my arm once more, this time pulling me into a sitting position before he lost his footing. I fell backward again. I had no will to move.

"I'm leaving you," Steita shrieked. "There will be trouble if you stay. I won't accept it for you."

I did not answer, although I could tell that Steita was deeply afraid for himself if he left me behind. He pulled me forward again, and again my body fell backward to the hard-packed earth.

"I'll be right back," I heard Steita say and then I heard him run off. I listened a moment longer and then slipped into unconsciousness.

CHAPTER SIX
SEPARATE PATHS

I awoke early. My body ached as I turned on the shaggy sleeping-fleece. My legs and arms were stiff, and my chest felt as if it had been struck a heavy blow. I moaned, gradually coming to my senses, and the memory of the Lama plunging his hand into my chest returned. It had not been a dream. Slowly, I moved my hand over my chest and paused, relieved to feel a beat beneath my clothing. I still had a heart, at least, although the pain reminded me of the Lama ripping it from me, standing above me with my heart dripping in his hand. The memory made me shudder. Beneath closed eyelids, I could still see the thin, red thread.

It was as if the red thread joined the Lama and me. I opened my eyes again and tried to move but I was too sore.

"Milarepa, look at me." Thither tilted my head to face him with his hands. His expression was anxious and worried. "Try to speak," he said again.

I felt I could not speak and shut my eyes. Immediately, I saw the red thread connected to me. It was pulled taut and I knew that, if I followed it with my inner vision, I would see the Lama Yungtun-Trogyal at the other end. Quickly, I opened my eyes again.

"What is it, Milarepa?" Thither asked.

I moved my lips but no words came out.

Thither slid his arm under my head and lifted me to a sitting position. I groaned. "Easy," he said, "easy does it."

I wanted to close my eyes but was afraid to do so. Instead, I looked at Thither, making every effort to keep my attention focused on him. "The blood," I said finally, glancing down at my chuba.

"What blood?" Thither asked. He was kneeling on the floor next to me, holding me in a sitting position. "I can see no blood. Perhaps you had a bad dream."

I tried to remember but I did not believe my experience with the Lama to be a dream. Following it, it seemed that I had slept a deep, death-like sleep that was without dreams. "I remember that you helped me back to our room," I said.

"Yes," Thither said, "you fainted during contemplation, or so Steita told me. Did they drug you?"

I shook my head. I wanted to tell Thither what had happened between me and the Lama but the mere thought of speaking it aloud made my chest hurt. I looked down at myself. The front of my chuba bore no blood stains.

"Did you believe yourself injured?" Thither asked.

I nodded, then turned and looked about the room. Nothing seemed different. The bare walls glared back at me. "Is Steita here?" I asked.

"No," Thither answered. "He left some time ago." He hesitated. "I did not speak with him this morning."

I relaxed, feeling easier that Steita was not there. "Will you help me to my feet?" I asked.

Thither rose to his feet and extended his hands to me, pulling me up. I could not help but moan in the effort. "Did they beat you?" he asked, gazing at me as I steadied myself on my feet.

"I will be all right," I said, not looking at him. Suddenly, I noticed that the skin covering our doorway had been pulled back. I wondered if anyone was in the hallway listening.

Thither stood still, watching me, then he said, "I am going to the village, will you join me?"

I turned my head to look at him. The worry on his face had been replaced by an urgency. Although he was the same tall, lean youth who had become my friend on the journey over the mountains, he had changed. Nowhere in his face could I see the carefree student. Something intense possessed him, as it did me. Although we did not speak of it, we both were aware of the change.

"I am going into the village today," Thither repeated. "Will you join me?"

I closed my eyes and opened them again. In that split second, I had caught a glimpse of the red thread connecting me to the Lama but I nodded that I would go just the same. At the decision, a sharp prickling sensation traveled from the base of my head to the middle of my back and stayed there. I sensed the presence of the Lama cautioning me. Lowering my eyes, I said that I would go now if he wished.

Thither stared at me as if he could sense an eerie presence about me. "Are you well enough to go now?" he asked.

I nodded.

"Then let us go," he said.

As we were about to leave, Steita returned and stood in the doorway. He appeared to be in a state of shock, standing and gaping at us with his mouth open.

"What is the matter with you?" Thither snapped when he saw him.

"I did not expect...," Steita stopped.

"You did not expect what?" Thither asked.

"That Milarepa would be up so early," Steita said. "I would have escorted him to morning prayers if I had known."

"Milarepa and I have business in the village," Thither said.

"Oh, but you must not leave the grounds," Steita said.

I could feel a tug at my chest but said nothing.

"Who told you that?" Thither asked.

Steita gestured with his hands, saying that it was not something that needed to be said by anyone. It was taken for granted that no one would leave without permission.

Thither hesitated and then went to his bed. He reached under the fleece skin mattress, withdrew a cloth envelope, and placed it carefully into the pocket of the trousers he had purchased from the innkeeper and his wife in Tsang. Then he turned and walked past Steita. I followed. The pain in my chest tightened and I did not dare look at Steita as I passed him.

We left the monastery grounds without attracting attention. We walked quietly. The weather was mellow and warm but overcast with intermittent patches of blue sky and occasional rays of warm light. There were others walking up the street, but when they saw me in the monastery robe, they stepped back and waited for us to pass. It was obvious that a chela from the Lama's monastery was someone to be suspected and feared. When we arrived at the marketplace, Thither stopped and put a hand on my arm. "Your wish is coming true, my friend, and I think we should celebrate it."

I paused and looked at Thither, observing the concern in my friend's face. I nodded. "It is true," I said, "the Lama is granting my desire."

Thither stopped and searched my face with compassion. I did not appear to be one who was fulfilling his mission in life, rather, I appeared to be one who was ending it. "Let's get something to eat," Thither said lightly. He looped his arm through mine and walked with me between the stalls of merchants to an open fireplace where a woman was roasting some meat over the flames. A strong, pungent odor filled the area. Thither pinched his nostrils together with his thumb and forefinger and laughed, pointing to the substance that was being used as fuel for the fire.

"What is it?" I asked quietly.

"Since there is little brush growing at this elevation, they use the yak dung for cooking fires," Thither said laughing. "It is another reason for us to return home quickly. All the food here tastes like yak dung, or haven't you noticed?"

"I have noticed," I answered but I did not smile. I was thinking of the cooking fires my mother and sister Peta made. In my village where the air was not as thin or high, there were rhododendrum and sage branches to be used for fuel. The morning that I had left Nyang, my beloved Zesay had been cooking a stew over sage brush. I wondered if Zesay guessed the penalty I would have to pay for power. Thither sat down on a haystack and touched my arm, motioning to me that there was another seat next to him. Then he held up some money to the woman tending the fire and told her that we wanted to eat. He turned to me again. "I do not belong at the monastery," he said sincerely.

I looked at my friend uneasily, not wanting to hear what I

sensed would follow. I thought of arguing with him but I knew that, in all fairness, I should say nothing.

"I wanted to come to the monastery to learn what I could, to round out my education so that I could better understand the higher teachings," Thither said, pausing again to look deeply into my eyes. "I don't think I have the stomach or the heart for the monastery of the Lama Yungtun-Trogyal," he added.

I was caught by Thither's reference to not having the heart for the life at the monastery and lowered my eyes. If I had had Thither's good fortune and interests, I knew I would not have chosen to stay either. "I understand," I answered without looking up.

"I wish to understand the power you seek," Thither went on, "but I do not seek it for myself. I have no desire to acquire it."

"That is wise," I answered. I raised my eyes to Thither's. "Once acquired, I am told it will consume."

Thither searched my face as if trying to discover the depths of the silent suffering that had settled on me since the contemplation exercise of the night before. "Can you tell now what happened to you?" he asked.

I started to say that I could not tell him, but hesitated. After a moment, I explained the connection that had formed between the Lama and myself; that I could actually see the thin red thread connecting us when I closed my eyes. Then, I stopped. The pain in my chest had become unbearable, forcing me into silence.

"How will you live with the pain?" he asked, apparently sensing it.

I raised my eyes to meet my friend's compassionate gaze. "I am told that I will not be able to live with the pain; that I will achieve the goal of avenging my family and forfeit my life in payment."

"But there must be some other way," Thither said quickly.

I did not answer. Again, I looked away. The woman at the cooking fire looked at us as she stirred the stew. I felt that she had heard our conversation. "Will you stay awhile?" I asked hopefully, not daring to look up for his reply.

"No," Thither said, shaking his head.

The cook interrupted, handing each of us a sharp stick wrapped in meat and dough, and a bowl of gruel. We bit into the meat while the bowls of gruel rested on our knees. Initially, the smell was noxious, but the taste was pleasant. We ate in silence, occasionally wiping the grease, which dribbled from the eating stick down the sides of our arms, onto our clothes.

"Where will you go?" I asked finally, not wanting to ask how soon Thither would leave.

"Do you remember as we were crossing the mountain into Tsang that I pointed to a green valley off to the north called Nar?" Thither asked.

I nodded. "Where the holy man lives," I said.

"Yes," Thither said, turning to look at me. "Marpa, the translator, lives there. I have decided to go to him and to stay until I learn all that I can." He hesitated. "The path of evil is not for me," he added. "It makes my flesh crawl. I suppose I always knew I wouldn't fit in." He shrugged his shoulders.

Filled with mixed emotions, I did not say anything for a long while. "When will you go?" I asked finally, realizing that the question already hung between us. I did not want my friend to leave and yet I knew that my life at the monastery would leave little time for friendship. It was best for both of us that Thither left.

"I have already gone," Thither said uneasily, searching my eyes for understanding. "When we left the monastery, I brought what money I had with me. When we are finished here, I will leave to find the translator Marpa in Nar."

I drew in a deep breath and slowly let the air out, trying to curb a sudden rise in emotion. I had grown accustomed to Thither, had learned to cherish his friendship and rely on his presence. He had only just arrived at the monastery and now he was leaving. A sudden pain in my chest reminded me that I could not afford sentiment and then a strange feeling overtook me. I became angry, although I tried not to show it.

Thither grimaced as though he felt the pain as well. "Be careful, Milarepa," he said fondly. "Above all, do not feel doomed. Regardless of what is told you, when your deeds are done, join me. There is a bond between us." He paused and then added, "No doubt we have earned the right to meet again."

I was struck by the condescending tone of Thither's words and remained looking at him. It was obvious that he felt himself to be above evil and the teachings of the Lama Yungtun-Trogyal.

I thought of my aunt and uncle and the way they often spoke to my mother.

"We will meet again," Thither repeated. He held the sharp eating stick out in front of him and gently shook it in salute. Beads of grease dropped away. He ate the remaining piece of meat and dough from it and threw the stick to the ground, wiping his hands on his trousers. "At least you won't be so hungry at the monastery tonight," he said, grinning playfully.

"You think Marpa will feed you any better?" I asked, in retort. I was torn, both grateful that he was leaving and angered by it.

Thither shrugged. "It doesn't really matter," he said. "What matters is that I will not be a square wheel with him. I knew the moment I set foot on the monastery grounds that I couldn't stay at that place."

I stared at my friend, trying to remain calm, and again the restraint filled me with feelings of loneliness. The more I felt, the greater the pain in my chest became, and I did not wish to show it. If I had been alone, I would have cried out. Thither seemed to be speaking to me from a great distance. He was trying to make me understand why he had to move on, something I already knew. I realized how badly he felt for leaving me. I thought of Zesay and how, when she had felt guilty about doing something I did not like, she would go to great lengths to explain her feelings to me. I was annoyed but tried to control the feeling, until the pain intensified, seemingly burning a hole in my chest. Then I looked up.

The woman stepped away from the cooking fire with two more sticks covered with meat and mush. "You want more?" she asked, interrupting, holding the food in front of our faces.

We looked at each other, shook our heads and handed her our empty bowls.

The woman gestured unpleasantly to Thither and then cast a sideways glance to me before returning to her cooking fire.

Thither rose to his feet. "Well, it is time I was on my way," he said. "I hope to find Marpa before dark and to sleep by his fire this evening."

I rose to my feet as well but said nothing. I glanced at the woman who was chatting with someone at the next stall. I felt very alone but grateful that the pain in my chest was gone.

"Well, my friend," Thither said, embracing me, then stepping back to look at me, "take care of yourself until we meet again."

I nodded. "And you, as well," I answered. I lowered my eyes for a moment to control the sudden rise of emotion. "As you said, we will meet again."

"Indeed, we will," Thither said, pleased to hear the words from me. He stood back and raised a hand to wave farewell.

I waved as well, watching as Thither turned and walked away from me. He did not look back.

*"Anger turned inward
becomes depression."*

CHAPTER SEVEN
THE SECRET OF POWER

One afternoon there was a commotion on the monastery grounds. I paused to watch the movement of monks, their grey robes shifting back and forth, as if blowing in the wind, but there was no wind. From a distance, the scene was an eerie one and I could understand how the villagers, upon seeing such a sight, could fear those who wore the robes. The robes seemed to flutter and rise into the air like grey butterflies and then settle to the ground again. Hesitantly, I moved closer.

Most of those assembled were novices with a few acolytes among them, and as I approached, they all seemed to notice me and stood back on either side of the walkway to let me pass. I looked from face to face, but recognized no one. Moving with great effort, as though my feet were weighted to the ground and someone was pushing me from behind, I entered the circle. I wanted to run, to resist, but the muscles in my chest constricted. The pain was terrible, forcing me to continue. I tried to relax. The skin at the back of my neck prickled. Those gathered bowed to me, motioning that I should continue further into their depths. I moved slowly, gradually inching my way among them. When there was nowhere else to go, I turned and boldly looked around.

My vision was confused. For an instant, it seemed I was transported to a faraway place, watching them from a distance, unafraid. And then, my perception shifted and I was suddenly among them again. Each raised his arms and twirled, the skirts of the grey robes weaving back and forth. They seemed to move as a unit about me, weaving, and leaping high in the air with outstretched arms. I felt uplifted, as though flying with them, and when, at last, they settled to earth, I settled with them. I felt like a butterfly fluttering through the air with other butterflies. The word illusion came to mind and I considered the villagers and their fear of the monastery residents, guessing that much of their fear was based on illusion, events such as this that had been witnessed by them.

"In part, that is true," a voice said from behind me.

I spun on my heels, coming face to face with Narquin.

"It is true that you witnessed a physical exercise," Narquin said, "but you also witnessed a mental exercise that created the illusion of butterflies in an active wind."

I was too astonished to speak. I stared at Narquin in disbelief, wondering if indeed the man knew my thoughts.

Narquin smiled.

I started to look away but was drawn to the sensitive features of his finely chiseled face. There was something about him that was distinctly different from anyone else. He was no mere man.

"And neither are you," Narquin said aloud, answering my thought. He paused, gazing at me. A light mist seemed to form between us, and in it, the face of another was superimposed on his face. It was the face of the great Lama Yungtun-Trogyal.

I shivered and lowered my eyes.

"You see who it is that binds us," Narquin said.

I nodded but did not speak. An image of the Lama loomed forward in my mind, and for an instant, there was nothing else in all the world. I purposely kept my eyes averted, not wanting to meet Narquin's gaze even though I felt it full upon me.

"You need not feel uncomfortable in my presence," Narquin said. "Since you have been granted the means to gain power with which to fulfill your purpose, it is my task to guide you to the knowledge that will fill you with power."

I kept silent.

"As you assume the power, I will remain with you," Narquin said. His eyes seemed to reach into me as he said, "Wherever you go, I go; whatever you do, I do."

As he finished speaking, the muscles in my chest constricted. For a moment, I believed I might double over in pain, but then the inner grip was released. With the release came the prickling sensation at the back of my neck again, and I lowered my eyes.

Narquin smiled. "The power was performed for you this day," he said, motioning to the monks who had danced about me. They were now still, waiting for instructions. At a signal from Narquin, they began to dance again, leaping and twirling into the air.

I watched, caught by the wonder of appearances and how things seemed to be one thing and yet were of an entirely different nature.

"Remember, they are both one thing and another," Narquin said, answering my thought. "There is no such thing as one thing *or* another. All things are all things. Illusion is both real and unreal, as it is perceived through the eyes of the beholder." He paused, gazing at me. "When you understand this, you will have grasped the great secret of power." He paused again. His eyes were deep pools and I felt lost in them. "Do not forget this moment," he said. "Go now! Experience the illusions of your mind. Gaze inwardly at it and be sure of its nature. Ask yourself if what you see and feel contain power over you. You will know it, if by looking at the power and feeling the power, the experience is accompanied by fear. Fear means that the power has turned inward, facing you. Should this happen, you must find a way to reverse it immediately; otherwise, it will consume you." He then continued. "It is this inward consumption by power that ails the people of this village and the masses of people everywhere. They view power and recognize it as addressing them, coming towards them, and they crumble in spirit. Their lives fill with chaos, and the chaos spreads as a plague, creating havoc, and argument, and war in its wake." Narquin stopped, studying the intense expression on my face. His eyes narrowed, and his handsome facial features seemed pinched and threatening. "Never look at the power, Milarepa," he said in a soft voice. "The trick is to turn the power outward, away from you, and then you become suddenly in complete control of it—over everyone and everything in your environment. You can use this power to create a hailstorm to destroy your aunt and uncle's crops, and with it you can cut off the lineage of their descendants. It is easy to murder." He stopped, grinning at my shocked expression. "The possibilities are endless," he added.

I stared at Narquin, unable to speak. So much of what he said reminded me of lessons related by Zesay from the good Lama Kataka. How could good and evil sound so much the same? Narquin smiled, sending a thrill into me, which started at my feet and moved slowly up the back of my legs, settling somewhere in the middle of my spine. For a brief instant, my confusion turned to understanding and then faded.

"Go among the monks," Narquin instructed. The lines of his young face were stern and firm as he gave me his order. "Practice with them. Experience the flight of illusion with them. When you understand it, then find me and tell me what you have learned." He motioned for me to go and join them.

I turned. The sight of the monks and their grey robes flying about them met me and, gradually, as I watched, I sensed a definite rhythm to their movements, as though they were dancing together to a silent tune. Reluctantly, I moved into the circle of flying grey robes and took my place among them. They twirled about me. The rhythm of their movements was intense, so captivating that I could not keep still. I found myself imagining butterflies, and as I did, I was aware that I had raised my arms and was leaping into the air with the others. My robe blew in the windless wind, obeying the commands of my movements. I had the sensation of fluttering in flight, and for a brief time, I felt as though I had become a butterfly. I was experiencing the flight of illusion as Narquin had instructed me to do. As I danced, I tried to recognize the illusion and how it performed for me. I knew that it was of my own making, but I also knew I was not alone in the making of it. Each monk was seeing himself as a butterfly and was caught up in its flight. Was it because there were many seeing the same image of themselves that I was able to see the same thing? And, if that were true, were my feelings and movements independent of the others' or were they caused by the others'?

The dancing stopped. I quickly looked around. The others had disbanded and were moving away, walking solitarily toward the entranceway of the huge stone monastery. Had someone signaled them? I looked about but saw no one. Then, seemingly out of nowhere, I saw Steita running toward me, the skirt of his grey robe held tightly in one hand so as not to trip himself.

"Milarepa....Milarepa," Steita called, nearing me.

I waited.

Steita rushed to my side, his eyes ablaze with excitement. "We have been assigned together," he blurted out.

I stared at Steita, uncertain of what he meant, waiting for him to tell me.

Steita suddenly controlled himself. "I am sorry to hear about Thither," he said calmly.

I nodded, uncertain what he knew and annoyed that he would mention him. I had had no time to tell anyone of Thither's departure, and I doubted that Thither had said anything to anyone.

"He did not belong here," Steita said. He shrugged. "You know, he wasn't really one of us."

"What do you know about Thither?" I asked, impatiently.

"That he left," Steita said, suddenly humbled. "He was a holy man, not a sorcerer. He didn't belong with us."

I studied Steita's face. There was always something hungry and unfulfilled about the way he looked, something that irritated me. I remembered the first time we met. Steita had brought me tainted food when I was in the two-headed serpent chamber, and when I refused it, he asked to eat it. The fact that he didn't know that the food was tainted didn't change the way I felt about him. I was sure that I could never trust Steita, although I couldn't explain the feeling to myself.

"Narquin told me about Thither's leaving," Steita said with a sense of authority. "Narquin also told me that we have been assigned together."

I caught an excited look in Steita's eyes. I knew it was because he was frightened by Narquin and now felt honored by him. "You and Narquin?" I asked, sarcastically, knowing that that was not what Steita meant. I meant to hurt him.

Steita shook his head. "Oh, no," he said uncomfortably. "Not me and Narquin. You and I have been assigned together."

"Why is that?" I asked, not wanting to give in.

"He didn't say," Steita said. His original excitement at the news was replaced by embarrassment caused by my obvious lack of enthusiasm.

"What does it mean.....being assigned together?" I asked, wondering what Narquin had in mind. Already Steita and I shared the same bedchamber.

"We are to go to the prayer hall together," Steita said, regaining his sense of authority. "But perhaps since you are new to the monastery, you have not heard of it." Steita paused, waiting for a reaction.

"No," I answered, eyeing him. It occurred to me that Steita would be an easy informant to Narquin, although I didn't know why an informant would be necessary. Narquin seemed to know my every thought.

"The prayer hall is a magical place," Steita said, leaning toward me and lowering his voice. "It is where the secret rituals and incantations are stored. One is only allowed in there with the Lama's permission."

"Rituals and incantations for what?" I asked, lowering my voice as well.

Steita glanced about to see if anyone was near, then he leaned even closer to me and whispered, "Power...rituals and incantations for power."

*"All things are all things.
Illusion is both real and unreal,
as it is perceived through the
eyes of the beholder."*

CHAPTER EIGHT
THE PRAYER ROOM

Steita led the way to the rear of the main monastery building, through a grove of small pine trees to a large oval opening in the side of the mountain. He paused, turning to me. His eyes were excited as they watched the surprised expression on my face. "Follow me," he said in a mysterious whisper, then turned to the mountain again.

I followed Steita through the oval arch. Inside, oil lamps glowed along the passage walls and I could see that the tunnel was constructed of stone and that the floors, too, were inlaid stone. The forbidding appearance of the tunnel, combined with sensations of dampness and cold, and coupled with the uncertainty of what to expect at the other end, made the hairs at the back of my neck stand out. A steady current of energy ran up and down my back. Ahead of me, Steita giggled nervously, as though recalling his own surprise when he had first been taken there. "Some say the passage is actually a tunnel through the mind," he said, in a soft but excited voice.

I didn't answer, unsure of what he meant. Steita glanced back at me and giggled again. I looked away, shifting my attention to the long, straight tunnel ahead. I was amazed at how long and straight it was, realizing that it must have taken years to complete.

"I helped in the construction of this passage," Steita said, as if tuned to my thought.

The tunnel seemed to have been there a very long time, and I doubted that Steita had had anything to do with it.

Steita stopped and turned to face me. "You don't believe me, do you?" he asked.

Surprised, I said nothing.

"The truth is, I have been at the monastery much longer than you think," Steita said, "years and years longer." His eyes narrowed in the telling.

"How long has it been?" I asked, not wanting to argue.

Steita opened his mouth and then closed it again. He grinned and shook his head, as if to say he could tell no more. He turned and continued down the tunnel.

We walked on for a short distance and arrived at a door.

"Here we are," Steita said, stopping before it. He turned to me and whispered, "This is the prayer room."

I was suddenly unnerved and tried to regain my sense of composure. Steita grinned at my uneasiness. I felt unbearably cold, as if the blood had drained from me, and I considered turning around and running away. An image of my mother held me to the spot. For a moment, I thought I heard her say something to me.

"Put your hands on the door and push with me," Steita said. "It is the law that all who enter must do so under their own strength."

I put my cold, nearly numb hands on the door and pushed, expecting resistance, but the door opened easily.

Steita was first to step into the chamber, and after he entered, he turned to look at my face.

The chamber was a large, well-lit room, illuminated by oil lamps along the base of each wall. Just above the lamps were wooden drums, decorated with red and black symbols. The drums turned slowly, making low, eerie, rumbling sounds as they moved. Above the drums, the walls were black and covered with murals. I studied the murals and found that they were not painted on the black wall but etched into it. Over one drum, the black wall was scratched into a scene of a man dressed in monk's robes who stood high on a mountaintop. His arms were outstretched toward a stormy sky. Below him was a village being attacked by hailstorms. The low, drum-like sound of the wooden barrel turning below it seemed to animate the scene. For a moment, I thought I recognized the monk on the mountaintop.

"This is the prayer room," Steita said in a normal voice. "The drums are prayer wheels, although larger than the ones we are used to seeing." He paused and watched me. "All the dreams and wishes of those favored by the great Lama are brought to life in this room."

I felt a slow chill and turned to come face to face with Narquin. He was wearing a long, black robe. I jumped in surprise.

Steita quickly turned and, seeing Narquin, bent at the waist in a deep, low bow.

"You may leave, Steita," Narquin said, coming forward. "You have done well."

Steita rose and obediently turned to leave.

"Bring Milarepa food and a sleeping-fleece," Narquin called out to him.

Steita paused, turning to Narquin in a respectful manner.

"And tell the kitchen monks that the food is for me," Narquin added.

Steita nodded and left.

Narquin turned to me. "As Steita has told you, this is the chamber of prayers." As he spoke, he made a sweeping gesture with his hands. "It is here you will learn how to manifest your desires." He raised his index finger before him. "Do you hear that low rumbling sound?" he asked.

I nodded and listened. The sound was indeed low and rumbling, but it seemed to have another quality, as well. It reminded me of the haunting whisper of the wind on a stormy day.

"The sound you hear," Narquin said, "is that of one's physical energies yielding to another's demands. It is the sound of a wish being accepted, of infiltrating into the magnetic field of an intended person, of unifying with it and becoming one with it. Herein lies the age-old secret of manifestation." He paused again, facing me. "More simply," he continued, "when you hear the current of energy running beneath the current of energy, you will know that your wish is being fulfilled."

"Am I to place my wishes in a drum?" I asked.

"That is why you are here. The usual practice is that when

one comes to the monastery, he is given an acolyte's robe and is left to himself for a period of time, usually many seasons. Finally, the acolyte is brought here to learn the secret of his desires. After that, he is made a novice." Narquin paused, then said, "In your case, an exception has been made. Since your mission is urgent, your life here has been hastened." He paused again. "But do not forget that once your mission is completed, when you have wielded the power of revenge and have punished your enemies, you must return."

My body shook in response to Narquin's words. I knew who he was but dared not think the name.

Narquin smiled as if he knew what I had been thinking. "I am the Lama in youthful form," he said. "I relive my youth because of the power it holds for the purpose of instructing those who require instruction and for collecting payment in return." His eyes suddenly became deep whirlpools, drawing me into them. "Your heart belongs to the Lama," he said. "Do you understand me?"

Again my body shook involuntarily as a cold chill passed through me. I had damned myself for my mother's satisfaction, and I knew there was no turning back. I would have to avenge my mother and forfeit my life in exchange. "I understand," I answered in a weak voice.

Narquin straightened and looked deeply into me. "You will stay here until you are ready," he said. "When you are certain that you have gained the power, you will leave. Return then to your village and have it out with the forces that have treated you unjustly."

I searched the firm lines of Narquin's face. His appearance was striking, almost handsome. His piercing, dark eyes and sharp features gave him a remarkable appearance, forbidding and isolated. I wondered what sort of man he had been before he had become a sorcerer, but quickly dismissed the thought. Narquin was no mere man. He was, in his own words, the youthful manifestation of the evil sorcerer.

Narquin nodded, aware of my thoughts.

"How long will it take me to prepare myself?" I asked.

"A short time," Narquin said thoughtfully, "or a very long time." He showed no expression.

"But I must hurry," I said.

"Then you will find a way to hurry," Narquin answered. "All

the tools are here in this prayer room. You must first learn to work with them. I cannot do it for you."

"Will you show me?" I asked quickly.

Narquin nodded and walked to the drums along the wall. He pointed first to the etching of a monk standing on the mountain, calling hailstones down on the village below. "Do you recognize the one in the picture?" he asked.

I stared at the picture, studying it. When I had first looked at it, I had thought the figure familiar, and now I was sure of it. "It is me," I said.

"Yes," Narquin said, "it is you. By your strong desires and purpose, you have found a way to etch yourself into the mission of this particular prayer wheel."

I stood silently staring at it, listening to the sound, aware that beneath the low rumbling sound there was also the eerie hissing of wind. I turned to Narquin. "Does this mean that I have this power now?" I asked.

Narquin stared at me for a long while before answering. "To use the power in any way is destructive," he said, "but to use it without control is sure disaster, not only for the intended, but for others and for yourself, as well."

"You have already told me that I am doomed," I said.

Narquin nodded that it was true. "But there is doom and there is doom," he said distantly.

I stared at the man, thinking suddenly of Zesay and how she had often spoken to me in similar riddles.

"To avenge your family will have one effect," Narquin continued, "but to avenge your family and murder many others in the doing will have a greater effect. It is one thing to settle a debt and another to incur a greater debt. It is the difference of your being doomed for this life alone or being doomed into eternity."

I was caught by the force of Narquin's words. Although I had never studied the scriptures of the ancients, Zesay had told me stories of men whose grievous misdeeds caused them to be turned into formless demons after their deaths, stories of how they were required to roam the earth forever without love or mercy. "How will I learn what I need to know?" I asked, looking at the prayer wheels, which turned slowly near the wall. There was one in the middle that did not move, nor was there a picture etched in the wall above it.

Narquin walked over to the prayer wheel that had caught my eye. "This one does not move because it is not motivated through use," Narquin said. "You are fortunate. Sometimes one has to wait a very long time to find a prayer wheel that is not in use. This one, it seems, is meant for you." He put his hand on the flat top surface and moved it down the smooth barrel-like side. It was red like the others and, on it, was written the same message: OM MANI PADME OM.

I studied the message, thinking how I had once believed that the meaning of it (in the jewel of the lotus) was something indicative of good. Now, I realized that it meant neither good nor bad, that it had nothing to do with goodness or evil, but that the message held the secret of the root of physical power. I turned and looked at Narquin, who was watching me, and I realized that he knew my thoughts. Neither of us spoke, but we gazed into each other's eyes for a long while. For the first time, I felt comfortable under Narquin's gaze, as though understanding the neutrality of the inscription on the prayer wheel had freed me in a way.

Narquin smiled. It was a gentle, kind smile and the sharp features of his rigid face seemed momentarily soft and pliant. It was a look of love and concern and there were tears in his eyes.

I felt tears in my eyes as well.

"OM MANI PADME OM," Narquin said softly.

I did not answer and yet, within myself, I repeated the very words Narquin had said.

"You will learn," Narquin said firmly. He turned and walked passed the prayer wheels. Each turned slowly, and above each, there was some image or picture on the wall. Some images were cruder than others, as if the hand that drew them lacked skill, but all the same, it was easy to see that the meaning of each was there. In each, a monk stood with outstretched arms, but the object of each was somewhat different. In one scene, the monk reached out to someone who had just murdered a man, woman, and children. In another, the monk reached out to a quivering, quaking earth on which many people were falling into a chasm. In another, the monk was reaching out to an image of himself sitting on a throne, above a gathering of people who were prostrated at his feet. Next to him were chests of coins and jewels. It was perhaps the most artistic of all the etchings and the most detailed.

Narquin motioned to others on the opposite wall. "And so it goes on and on," he said. "Most of the stories have similarities. Their individuality is hidden in their meaning to the ones who inscribed them."

"Are they the wishes of the monastery monks?" I asked.

Narquin shook his head. "Those who inscribed these murals are no longer here." He paused, then continued. "After a man has finished his etchings and has set his prayer wheel in motion," he must leave to act out the deed.

"And what happens when the deed is completed?" I asked.

"The prayer wheel stops," Narquin said. "Then someone like Steita or another chore boy enters and cleans that section of the wall so that someone else may use it."

I stared at the etching and then at the blank space reserved for me, before turning to Narquin again. "What happens to the monk whose wish has been fulfilled?" I asked uneasily.

Narquin shrugged his shoulders. "It depends," he said.

"On what?" I asked

"On the karma of his deed," Narquin answered.

"Please explain," I said.

"A deed that is not fully conscious lacks the power to save the one who puts it into effect," Narquin said, sighing as he spoke. "It is not greed that destroys the greedy, but their lack of concern for the nature of such lust."

"I don't understand," I said.

"I am trying to be plain-spoken," Narquin answered. "The trouble is, you are not aware of the nature of plain-spokenness. How then can I explain?"

"Please try," I prodded.

Narquin looked into my eyes for a long while before answering. "Your choice in life is a great one," he said finally. "Some men have nothing to push them beyond mediocrity. It takes a sense of purpose and mission to achieve great things. Yours is the choice of being a demon or a god." Narquin paused, looking deeply into my eyes.

I could feel the flow of Narquin within myself, like a rush of wind. The flow contained images of revenge and sensations that were demon-like. These I understood, but surely Narquin did not mean that if I turned my back on the revenge demanded of me by my mother that I would become god-like instead.

Narquin smiled. "You must kill because it is your task to kill. It is your mission. If you fail, your mother's scorn will follow you the rest of your life."

I knew that what he said was true and shook in the recognition of it. "In truth, life has offered me no choices," I said.

Narquin gazed deeply at me but did not speak.

I felt suddenly that I did have a choice but that I didn't understand it.

"When Steita returns with your food and bedding, you will be left here, sealed inside this room until your prayers are clearly recorded. Within the drum are some wooden tablets. Remove them and write your dreams on them. Then return them to the casket and etch your dreams onto the wall above it. When it is all accomplished, you will set the wheel in motion. It will then be time to leave—to align your actions with your dreams."

I placed my hand on the drum. It was heavy, and when I applied pressure, I could feel how difficult it was to turn it.

"The answer will come," Narquin said. "It is not a physical force that will set the drum into motion, but an invisible force, which is greater."

Narquin turned to leave, then hesitated, turning to me again. "I will shadow you," he said. "I will shadow you all the days of your life."

I felt suddenly sick, aware of a hollow space in my chest, and I looked away, touching the prayer wheel with my hands, as if trying to set it in motion. It turned just slightly and then stopped again.

"The wheels operate through your desires," Narquin said. He motioned to the other wheels. "They all move, according to the desires of their owners. One by one, they will all stop as their owners' desires are fulfilled." He hesitated, then went on, "the secret of setting the wheel in motion is something you will discover for yourself."

"That may take a long time," I said.

"Or it may take only a short time," Narquin added. He grinned. "I cannot say how long it will take you to fulfill your mission."

Narquin was about to leave when Steita entered, carrying a sleeping-fleece and a large container of food and water. He placed them on the floor next to me and then returned to the doorway for a second load. When he had finished, Narquin left and Steita followed him, pausing to glance back at me. He grinned as though he knew a great secret and then closed the door behind them.

I listened to the shuffle of their movements on the other side of the door. I knew, as I had been told, that I was being sealed into the chamber.

I stood alone in the prayer room, staring at the door through which Narquin and Steita had left. I wondered if the door was really sealed and, if it was, how I would open it when it was time for me to leave. I thought, too, of my experience with the door in the two-headed serpent chamber, how easy it had been to open and close it once I understood its operation. The memory satisfied me, and I turned to face the wall that held the image of myself in monk's robes standing high on the mountain. The scene showed the village below, and looking at it, I was certain that it was Nyang. The main structure in the picture was a red-domed tower like the one in my village. Studying it, I reflected on where Zesay lived not far from there. Her home was in the hailstone target area and it was conceivable that, if the storm was the same as on the wall, her home would be struck. She might even be injured in it. In a panic, I touched the wall where her house stood and rubbed the spot with the back of my hand, erasing it from the scene. I stood back and studied the picture again. It was plain to see that I had indeed removed that part of the scene from the wall, although there was no smear on my hand.

Touching it again, I felt the smooth texture of the wall and noted that, while smooth, it was also soft to the touch; it was covered with a thin layer of iron filings. They moved about the surface under the pressure of my hand. I picked a few of the filings from the wall and noticed that they resisted being removed, almost as if they were pulling from my touch. When I went to return them to the wall again, the filings jumped from my fingers and were reattached to the wall. Although I had never seen anything like it, I did recall a stone my sister Peta and I played with when we were small. Our father was still alive then and had given us a lodestone, explaining that it attracted certain types of filings and repelled others. The stone had been fascinating, as the wall was to me now.

How did my image and the image of my village come to be detailed in the filings on the wall? It seemed incredible. The wall was not a place where one etched an image with a finger or stick. It was easy enough to rearrange the filings to erase an image but to create one out of the countless minute filings was not a task for the hand. Testing this conclusion, I placed my little finger on the wall and tried to constructively rearrange a dense portion of the picture into the form of a house. It did not work. The blob of filings remained a blob. How then would I gain the control needed to succeed?

I stepped back from the wall and looked at the slow-moving prayer drum in front of the wall-picture. It moved at a definite pace, slow and steady, as though some invisible hand guided it. It seemed that the movement of the drum was connected to the picture. Taking a step back, I looked at the other pictures on the walls, noting that the prayer wheels next to them each moved at a different speed. I also noticed that there was one that, instead of rotating from left to right, rotated from right to left. The picture over it was that of a mass of air spiraling into the earth, with faces peering out of the spiral. I got a sick feeling as I looked at it, as though I could be sucked into it, and I quickly turned away.

The low rumbling sound of the turning prayer wheels seemed louder and more intense as I contemplated them. I moved slowly to the next wall, pausing before the only prayer wheel that was not in motion. Above it, the wall was clear-black and swept clean. Narquin had said that the space was for me, yet I did not know what to do with it.

I ran my hands over the smooth surface of the still drum, studying the bold inscription of OM MANI PADME OM and turned the drum around. Seeing an overlapping square on the side of it, I stopped it from turning and, sliding the panel open, I reached inside. Narquin had said that I would find tablets on which to inscribe my wishes. I felt around inside the drum and my hand touched some flat, loose objects on the bottom. Excited, I pulled them out. The tablets were inkboard writing tablets. Memories of my boyhood rushed at me. My mother had taught me how to use the inkboards when I was a very little boy and, while I hadn't had much use for them in my labor-filled life, I had many memories of Zesay using them. Zesay was always writing something, some thought the village Lama had shared with her, or some discovery she had made on her own.

I carried the tablets to the yak fleece Steita had brought and sat down. Next to me was a large basket, which had also been left. Opening it and looking inside, I saw that there was food and water, as well as a tiny gourd filled with ink and a brush. I pulled them out and placed them next to the tablets and looked at them for a long time.

I laid the tablets out in front of me. There were three tablets for three wishes. In the way that my mother had taught me, I carefully opened the lid on the gourd and dipped the brush into it, then smeared a layer of ink on one of the tablets. When I had finished, I held it up to my lips and blew on it to dry the ink. When it was dry to the touch, I recoated the tablet with another layer of ink. Once done, I examined the finish for evenness and set it on the floor next to me to dry while I began coating the next one. When I had finished with all three and they had dried, I lifted one to study its smooth, black surface. While each of the three tablets could represent a separate dream or wish, there was no doubt what needed to be inscribed on the first tablet. Resting the tablet on my knee, I raised the brush and turned it around, setting the sharp point of the handle to the ink surface. Slowly, I scratched away the black ink, forming the symbols that spelled revenge for my mother and sister and the reclamation of our land and fortune. As I wrote the message, I envisioned my aunt wailing in grief as her children met with destruction, as her husband went insane, as her house and crops were destroyed by hailstorms. The images were vivid and filled with emotion. When finished, I felt strangely satisfied but also strangely weary, so weary that I paused to reflect on it. I was suddenly aware that the curse had begun.

I put the tablet on the floor and picked up the second one. Immediately, I thought of Zesay. There was no doubt I was doomed. The Lama had told me so, and Narquin had reminded me of it. The Lama had my heart. There was no way it could belong to Zesay, as well. Yet I wished that Zesay could find fulfillment in living, that her beautiful countenance could be polished by a greater love than I could give. Raising the second tablet, I inscribed a wish for Zesay's happiness and placed it on the floor next to the first.

I picked up the third tablet and sat staring at it for a long time. It was my last wish, and although I knew that I was doomed, I wished that something fruitful would come of my doom. I wished that if I could have nothing, that my state of nothingness could serve humanity in some way. I wished that I could have true knowledge of my nothingness, of my being or non-being, and this is what I etched onto the last writing tablet. I then placed it on the floor next to the others and put down the brush. When I was certain they were dry, I gathered up the three of them and went to the prayer wheel. Carefully, I checked each one over once more, reading each for clarity as I placed them into the drum. I then slid the panel shut. I had a sudden feeling of relief, and I turned away.

Instantly, drawn by an inner urge, I quickly turned around again. The prayer wheel was turning slowly, and above it, on the wall, pictures were forming. The pictures were images of the wishes I had written on the tablets. It was as if the scenes I had seen in my imagination were being depicted on the wall. Witnessing them, I felt a great power stir within myself, a power directly connected to my imagination, to the feeling of the images in my imagination. It was a new feeling to me, and I sensed I was just beginning to discover the greatness of it.

I watched as the thin, delicate filings made a precision drawing of the thoughts I had held earlier, and I had a sudden sensation that, in reality, I was dreaming what I was seeing; that it wasn't really happening, although I knew that it was. The picture on the wall was complete in every detail. My thoughts had been the artist, had actually manifested the tablets in the prayer wheel. It was a miracle, and yet, as a miracle, the reality came from within myself, not from without.

I searched the picture on the wall. It was plain to see my first two wishes—for my family and for Zesay. I paused to admire Zesay's beauty, realizing that her beauty was locked in the way I imagined her. Everything I saw in the picture—the evil, the destruction, the beauty—was all a part of the way I had imagined it. I was staring at a product of my imagination and, as such, I was staring at myself. I was the evil, the destruction, and the beauty I saw, as well.

The realization struck me, and I put my hands out to the prayer wheel and lightly touched it as it turned in slow, even motion.

The nothingness I had wished for myself was inlaid in a mysterious part of the picture. I could not grasp it. There was something there, some images that I could not make out. It was as if they were not formed in form, as if there was nothing solid about them, only indications of something that was really nothing, a formless something of nothingness. I drew a deep breath, recalling Narquin's parting instructions. Now that the prayer wheel was in motion and the images had formed on the wall above it, I was to leave the monastery and return to Nyang. Although I was tired, I did not dare return to the yak fleece. There seemed to be no time for the luxury of sleep. I had completed my work quickly, and it was time for me to leave. I wrapped some food in a sack and went to the door, which easily opened at my touch. I felt my body shiver, as though some icy liquid had been poured down my back, and I stepped outside.

CHAPTER NINE

UNLEASHING OF POWER

I stood on the hillside above my village, looking down at it. I recalled the image of myself on the prayer room wall, how in those pictures, I had also stood on a hillside above Nyang.

It was late afternoon and the sun was high in the heavens. As I looked out over the terrain, I saw that workers were returning home from working in my aunt and uncle's fields, and I saw that the crops of vegetables and barley were nearly ripe for harvest. Studying the area, I saw my mother's house. Seeing no movement about the place, I supposed that she and Peta were inside. I looked to the far right at the house in which Zesay and her parents lived. It was behind the red tower. I was surprised to see that a new structure had been built next to the tower. It, too, had a red dome on it, although it was nowhere as high.

Had I been gone so long that a new building could have been planned and built in my absence? I had lost all track of time. Gazing down on the structure, I noticed that the villagers passed by the addition casually, as if they had already grown accustomed to its presence.

I lifted the hood on my robe to cover my head and shade my eyes from the late afternoon sun. For a long while, I thought of nothing, merely staring into the village that had been my village, feeling the multitude of memories gathered about it, enraptured by simply having returned home.

Gradually, I became aware of my purpose in being there again. If I had had no mission, if I was merely returning home, I would have run down the steep path and shouted with joy. My mother, however, had extracted a promise from me that I would return with the power to avenge my family, and I knew there could be no welcome for me until my duty was fulfilled.

Seeing the Lama in my mind's eye, I raised my arms over my head, palms extended to the quiet village below me. I recalled the prayer room; the prayer drum that contained my wishes turned slowly in my thoughts. I shifted my attention to the wall above the drum, where the image of myself had been standing on the hill over Nyang, gathering in the terrible dark clouds and crashing thunder, calling forth giant hailstones to rain from the black sky. I recalled, too, how I had erased a part of the storm so that Zesay's home would be untouched and how, with the motion of my fingers on the pliable filings on the wall, I had directed the entire hailstorm upon my aunt and uncle's crops, their home, and their daughter and son-in-law's home.

The storm raged and built in power as I remembered the many painful expressions I had seen on my mother's face through the years. I remembered how, even when she was very sick and could barely stand, delirious with fever, she had forced herself to work in the fields so that her children would have food to eat that night. I was eight-years-old then, and I had pleaded with my aunt to allow me to work in my mother's place, but she had refused me, saying that I was too small to be of much value.

I was not too small now. I would repay my aunt for her cruelty. I would destroy the crops that she so valued over my mother's well-being, over any human life. I would punish her by destroying her house. I thought of my uncle, the weak-minded husband of the cruel aunt. I hated my uncle for his weakness in allowing himself to be manipulated by his evil wife. The man had become less than human in self-esteem, deserving a stature lower than the humblest animal. Their only child, now a grown woman, was almost a copy of my aunt. She had married an insecure man very much like my uncle. It was plain to see that the daughter meant for her husband to be like her father. She often ridiculed him privately and publicly and assured him that their children would do the same. It had been my mother's wish that the daughter be killed or maimed in such a way that she could bear no descendants.

I stood on the hill, filled with the passion of my mother's hatred and a desire to appease my own. I raised my arms higher, stretching with palms forward, my fingers curled like talons, attacking the black clouds overhead. It was as if I could feel my fingers penetrating the fabric of the ethers; that I was ripping through some unseen part, as slowly, ever so slowly, I felt my passion ripple through me. It started at my feet and traveled up the back of my legs, up my spine, and passed through my arms. My fingertips stung as if someone had touched each one with fire. The hood fell from my head, exposing it to the dark sky. I had a feeling of intense pressure building in me, and I knew that either it would find release or that it would consume me.

The wind began. It came gradually at first and then gathered force. Suddenly, my robe was lifted by it and pulled tightly about my lean body. It pulled, released, and thrashed against me, traveling up and around me. I knew I had somehow unleashed the awful power my anger and hatred had accumulated. In that moment of knowingness, the wind obeyed the direction of my curled fingers, and as I lowered them toward the village of Nyang, the fury of the tempest broke free, and the wind was joined by bolts of lightning and roaring claps of thunder.

People in Nyang began to run. I watched, and when finally I saw that everyone had run a safe distance from my aunt and uncle's fields, I relaxed, permitting the awful torrent that had been raging through me to go free. The power was unleashed, free to travel out of me to where I directed my attention in the village below.

Huge hailstones poured upon the fields of Nyang, and their thunderous sounds were mixed with eerie screams and the whistle of the wind, streaks of lightning, and thunder. Nothing but the anger of the elements was visible for that time, ignited by my own, easing only as the tension in me eased, until gradually, it stopped. It was then that I saw what I had done.

The village streets were covered with hailstones, and

everywhere I looked, white rocks had settled. The fields, where my aunt and uncle's crops had been, were now solid white. Not a single plant survived the torrent, and I was pleased to see that both my aunt's house and her daughter's were nearly destroyed. It was difficult to see details, but from the hill, I could see that one side of the daughter's house had been knocked from its pilings.

I relaxed my fingers and lowered my arms. In my unfocused gaze, I saw people stepping outside their homes; at the same time, my inward vision was confronted by Narquin. As if in a dream, I fought to focus on one or the other, trying to determine the real from the unreal but the two seemed the same.

Narquin's countenance changed to the Lama Yungtun-Trogyal's and back again. As the same person, one image overlapping the other, they looked directly at me and, in turn, I saw myself, in inward vision, looking at them. It seemed they were laughing at me, and I was laughing at myself. The laughter was astonishment at the release of power. After a moment, they stopped laughing, studying me compassionately. I felt suddenly weak and humbled by their gaze.

"You have achieved your mission," Narquin's voice said, rising above the changing images of himself and the Lama Yungtun-Trogyal. "It would be wise for you to return to the monastery now. Returning will save you from greater doom."

I rejected the warning, focusing my attention on the streets of Nyang. People were weeping and wailing in the streets. Tears came into my eyes, clouding them. I knew that I had injured many and was suddenly ashamed. I had to know who I had harmed, and I had to give assistance to those who needed it. Turning around, I started down the trail that led to the village.

The sun was again shining when I stepped off the trail into Nyang. I saw at once that the hail had melted into tiny pebbles and that, in many areas, it had completely disappeared. People were sweeping the streets and the walkways to their homes.

Many houses were scarred by the storm, but none appeared to be seriously damaged, and no one appeared injured. Yet the wailing I had heard from the hill, though softer, was still audible. As I passed, I noticed that people looked at me with fear in their eyes.

I reached out and touched the arm of a man who was repairing a window covering on his house. The man was one I knew, whom I had known since childhood, and yet the man, upon seeing me, drew back in horror.

"Hello, Perioa," I said kindly. "I have returned to my mother. I hope she is well." I paused, motioning to the house off in the thicket. None of the bushes around my mother's house had been damaged in the storm.

"How could you do this to your friends?" Perioa snapped, recovering from his initial shock.

I stared at the man, uncertain if I had done anything at all or if my passion had paralleled a freak of nature. The storm now seemed absurd and dreamlike, a timely feat of nature that had nothing to do with me. "You accuse me?" I asked.

The man pointed to the robe I was wearing. "You wear the chuba of the evil ones," Perioa said. "I have heard that your mother sent you to learn the ways of revenge, and you have done it. Only now," he said, spitting the words between his teeth, "it is too late."

"What do you mean?" I asked, feeling that I was about to awaken from my dream.

"Instead of appeasing your mother's hatred, you harm only those who have cared for you," Perioa said.

"I meant no harm to you," I said, sincerely. "To prove it, I will stay and help you repair the damage. I will stay and work for you," I repeated, turning about to the other homes in the area and motioning with my hand, "I will work for you and for everyone until everyone is satisfied."

Perioa shook his head. "It cannot be done," he said, "and it is all for nothing."

"Not for nothing," I said angrily, returned to the reality of what I had intended to do. "My mother and sister have suffered all these years because our land and fortune were stolen by my aunt and uncle. Now I have destroyed my aunt and uncle's crops, ruined their house and their daughter's house. My mother will have her land again."

Perioa stared at me. His expression softened, and he nodded. "It is true that you have destroyed your aunt's crops," he said, "but your mother has gained nothing by the revenge."

"She will not think that way," I said, starting to leave.

"It doesn't matter anymore," Perioa called out.

I paused, staring at my mother's house in the distance and thinking that I should have gone directly there instead of exchanging words with Perioa. The man was not in his right mind.

"It doesn't matter," Perioa said again, "because your mother is dead."

I turned around and stared at the man in disbelief. It could not be true.

"Your mother is dead, and your sister Peta has gone to the city of Katmandu to seek employment," Perioa said again. "I am sorry to tell you this, but someone has to, and I doubt any of the others will dare to speak to a man of the evil order."

I was too overcome to respond.

"The worst part for us is that you have destroyed the crops that feed us," Perioa said, once again with an angry voice. "In destroying your aunt's life, you have destroyed ours, as well. What will we eat this winter? Many of us will have to leave."

I started toward my mother's house.

"I wouldn't stay long," Perioa called after me. "You are safe as long as everyone still suffers enough to be afraid of you, but when the shock of what has happened wears off, they will kill you."

I did not answer but kept walking.

"I would kill you myself," Perioa called angrily, "but why dirty my hands on you? You are damned anyway."

I paused before the entranceway to my mother's house. The skin Zesay's father had hung in the doorway to protect the house from the elements was hanging loose on one side, and grasses and other weeds had grown over the entrance, making it plain to see that no one had entered or left the house in a long time.

Hesitantly, I stepped through the weeds, pushed the skin aside, and entered the old house. It was dark. A strong, damp, musty odor greeted me, and for a moment, I had the feeling that I had entered a mountain cave rather than the house in which I had spent my childhood. I went to the window and lifted the hard, dried-out skin that covered it.

Rays of sunlight poured into the small house. Cobwebs hung loosely, draped from the stove to the cooking pot where I had often watched my mother and Peta preparing supper. What little furniture there was had been upturned, and items, which were once considered important personal possessions, were scattered about the dirt floor.

I reached down to pick up a wooden box, and as I did, I saw that in the shadow next to it, there was something else. I stooped down next to it and then fell to my knees, my monk's robe suddenly binding me.

Stretched out on the floor next to the box was a skeleton. I was dumbfounded by the sight, and looking at the corpse, I was filled with awe and discomfort. Then, looking at it, I recognized my mother's gold ring on the hand nearest the wooden box. I realized, suddenly, that the corpse in front of me was my mother's corpse. I let out a cry and covered my eyes with my hands, weeping.

How had it happened? When Perioa had said that my mother had died, I had believed that she had died from disease, that her corpse would be properly disposed of in the customary manner. But to leave her corpse within the house meant that she had released her spirit from her body by her own hand. My mother had committed suicide. Why? Had she believed that I would fail her? Had I been gone so long that she had given up hope?

The questions that came to mind tormented me. Had my aunt made life so unbearable that she could not live for my return? Thinking of my aunt, I cursed her. I wished all of my feeling upon her, all of my pain, and I wished, too, that she would share in the doom that awaited me in the future. Seeing her plainly in my imagination, I was certain that she would suffer on my account, and the knowledge gave me a small amount of solace.

I removed my hands from my eyes, looked at my mother's skeleton, and then slowly rose to my feet, stumbling as the length of my robe caught under my feet.

I went outside.

The villagers were gathered a short distance from my mother's house, watching, and as I stepped outside, they quickly turned away at the sight of me. Some even ran. I stepped into the street, thinking of Zesay and wanting to go to her, but afraid that my visit might endanger her.

"Better get out of Nyang," Perioa called out to me.

I turned to look at Perioa and then began walking slowly toward the edge of town. The villagers followed me and I was aware that, at the slightest provocation, they would stone me or beat me to death with sticks. I quickened my pace until I came to the path that led uphill to the area where I had unleashed the power, and then I turned back to look at them.

No one tried to follow me further. They stood staring after me until, one by one, they disbanded and returned to their homes. Watching them leave, I was overcome with the weight of my actions toward those I had known all of my life and, for a time, I felt I could not move. I began to weep. There was nothing for me now. My mother was dead. My sister was gone. I could never go to my beloved Zesay again, and all those who had once been my friends now hated me. I was responsible for the destruction of everyone's food and the cause of their difficult year ahead.

Filled with remorse, I untied the rope from around my waist and dropped it to the ground. Then I pulled the heavy grey robe up over my head and dropped it to the ground, as well. Naked, I brushed my hands over my body to removed the feeling of the coarse monastery cloth and shivered, both from the memory of it and from my nakedness without it. Without knowing where I would go, I finished the climb to the top of the hill and set out across the mountains. I knew I was to die.

What is despair?

"When all things are gone and there is nothing, despair can be mistaken for courage."

INTERLUDE
HUMHUMHUMHUMHUMHUMHUM**HUMUH**

Rechung paused in his story-
telling and turned to where Milarepa had been sitting, but the Guru
was not there. In his place, there was a writing tablet. Rechung
reached for it and held it up in front of him and read:

> Continue to sing the songs of my life. The next phase will
> give the people the hope they are seeking.

Rechung read the tablet aloud. There was a stir in the
gathering and then a sudden silence. It was as if they still saw
the Guru sitting before them. Again they settled back to listen to
Rechung's telling of the Jetsun's story.

PART TWO
FREEDOM

CHAPTER TEN
REUNIONS

The cold, mountain air stung my naked flesh. I moved slowly through the mountains forgetful of where I was going. Something within me resisted remembering, as though I was moving through a dream without concept of time or space. Horrible, fiendish images confronted me, threatening me like visions in a bad dream, and it seemed that nothing I could say or do to myself would cause me to awaken. I pinched myself. I hit my head with my fist. I lifted a rock from the ground and beat my chest with it, striking a blow so hard that the skin around my ribs was badly bruised and a trickle of blood ran down my stomach. I felt the pain and I saw the blood. I even tasted it to be sure of what it was, and yet I had the certain feeling that I was deeply asleep and could not awaken. Morning and night seemed to blend together, the dark air colder and more horrible than the light.

In the dark, the fiends of my nightmares became even more vivid. I saw an image of myself arriving at my mother's house and finding the entrance to it overgrown with weeds and vines. In my vision, I pushed them away and entered to find my mother's decayed corpse sprawled on the dirt floor. Looking at her, I wept, feeling her disgrace, wishing with all my heart that I could pour out my pain to

Zesay, knowing that she would find a way to comfort me. But Zesay was lost to me, and so was my sister Peta, who had left for the city of Katmandu to find a livelihood.

The odor of my mother's decayed flesh filled my nostrils as I stood on the mountainside. I felt sick and dizzy, my bare feet brutally damaged from stumbling on the hard, jagged rock. I wanted to scream, to hear the sound of the pain that filled me, but something within would not allow it.

The mountains stood around me in cold silence. I told myself that if I could shout, I would awaken. As it was, the dream damned me, forced me to hold to myself the cursed memory-like images of life, death, debauchery, and untouchable love, without outflow, trapped within me, like a sickness, a boil ready to burst on diseased flesh. Occasionally, in the silence, an insect chirped and mocked my silence.

I paused on the mountainside and rubbed my hands on the sides of my numb, naked body, trying to warm myself. The palms of my hands were rough and torn, and the feeling of them on my thighs and buttocks was abrasive, exchanging numbness for pain. Within myself, I shrieked. I withdrew my hands and held them up to examine them in the weak sunlight.

My hands were cut and bleeding, and gazing at them, I saw that my chest, arms, and legs were bleeding, as well, and that there was a gash alongside my penis. Becoming aware of it, I felt its pain above the rest, and again, I thought of my beloved Zesay.

Zesay had wanted to marry me, to journey with me to the monastery of the great and evil Lama Yungtun-Trogyal. She would have sacrificed herself for my love and for our union. It would have been a point of agony and ecstasy, and as I thought of it, my feelings were transmitted to the wound and my penis suddenly stood erect.

Had I no shame? Was I such an ignorant youth that I would enjoy such a fantasy with my beloved Zesay now, when there was nothing I could offer her?

The answer was quick in coming. If Zesay were to suddenly appear, I would seize her and plunge my agony into her in hopes of freeing myself from this misery. I would give it all to her, and I knew that she would take it, transform it, and give it back to me as love and understanding. She would heal my wounds as no other had the power to do. Zesay, my beloved, would take me to her breast and heal me with love.

"Zesay! Zesay!" I called, but I could not hear the sound of my own voice, and I knew that I was not calling aloud. It didn't matter anyway. Zesay was nowhere near. I fought to compose myself, to quiet the madman within, but the nightmare continued. I saw myself standing high on a hill over the village Nyang. I was standing there in monk's robes with my arms stretched above my head, shouting to the sky, demanding it to open. And I saw that the sky did open and a psychic part of myself, a power, reached into it and drew out a hailstorm, flinging it upon the village below. Again and again, I saw my aunt and uncle's crops destroyed and their home toppled. It was a sweet but bitter vision, filled with the satisfaction of avenging my family, coupled with the remorse for the destruction of the food supply that was to feed the people of Nyang. The famine ahead would be an added curse for me to bear.

Slowly, I turned and looked about the mountainside and down into the valley below. Beneath me was a valley so green that the mountains, with their grey-black rock, seemed to be a dividing line between two worlds. Staring down into it, I imagined the warmth and comfort of being in such a place. I remembered the journey through the mountains with Thither. Together, we had paused to look down into the Tsang Valley, to the village of Nar, where the great sage Marpa was reputed to have lived. Thither had wanted to go there then, but I had insisted on pushing on to our destination. I wondered if Thither had returned there after all, if he had found Marpa, and if the guru had met his expectations.

Gazing down at the valley floor, I recalled how Thither had referred to the guru as "the translator," saying that Marpa had made a copy of the ancient Naacal records, which were the spiritual teachings of an ancient people. Thither had been told by the Lama Kataka that the teachings held in Marpa's possession were the highest available to mankind. I tried to imagine what sort of man Marpa was, if he was the all-powerful guru that Thither had believed him to be, and wondered if, in some way, he would be able to help me free myself from my inner torment. I hesitated, unsure if I could safely descend the steep mountain, and then, reminding myself that, for the most part, I was already dead and had nothing to lose, I started down the rough terrain.

The way down was more hazardous than I could have imagined. There was much loose rock and nothing to hang onto. I moved slowly, a mere footlength at a time, squaring my back with the cliff to keep myself from falling to my death. Several times, my foot slid out from under me and I slipped, the crude, grey-black rock driving its rough surface along my back and buttocks. Once, as I fell, I felt my flesh tear and the bones along my spine crack. I could not stop the fall, and I believed I was done for, when suddenly I was caught by the gnarled branches of a small, spiny tree. I cried out as I fell into its arms. The branches had saved me, but they also tortured me, driving their finger-length thorns into my thighs.

I have no further memory of my descent. Driven by pain and trying to escape the unbearable clutches of it, I must have slipped from consciousness and fallen the rest of the way. The next thing I remember is opening my eyes on a carpet of cool, green, sweet-smelling grass. I was face-down. The air was cool but not cold, and as I became aware of a slight breeze trickling across my back, I tried to rise. An intense pain pushed me to the ground again, and I remained motionless, waiting for it to settle. When the pain subsided, I raised my head and turned my face to the side. The sun was shining high overhead and, for some moments, I was blinded by it. I heard laughter and strained to see into the brilliant golden light of the sun. Images were faint at first, but gradually, in the distance, I saw a road. Two women, each with a load of straw tied to her back, were walking side-by-side, talking and laughing. They were followed by an ox and cart.

I cried out, but my voice was weak. After a few moments, I lost consciousness again.

I awoke to the sound of a drum and opened my eyes. "He's awake," I heard someone say, and then there was the clatter of feet. A plump, middle-aged woman with a round face and small, kind eyes gazed down at me. "Now don't try to talk unless you're up to it," she said thoughtfully. "You've been through a bad time. For awhile, we were not sure that you would live." She smiled. "But you did!"

I smiled back, aware suddenly of a sharp pain in the side of my face. I straightened my expression again.

"There now, you don't have to smile," the woman said. "If you get well, that will be good enough for me." She gently wiped my face with a cool cloth. "Your pretty face is all cut up. You'll be left with a scar or two." She looked down at me.

I closed my eyes and opened them again. The light in the room seemed brilliant, so white that it hurt my eyes, and yet, it was a pleasant pain. I could see the woman only faintly. I knew she was watching me.

"My name is Nadar," she said, pleasantly, "and you are welcome here." She paused, studying me. My vision was clearing when she asked, "Are you ready for company?"

I blinked my eyes.

Nadar rose from her seat and went to the door. A moment later, someone else entered. As the person came close to me, the same sound of a drum that had awakened me earlier sounded again. I closed my eyes momentarily to rest them from the intense light, then I opened them again. It was Thither who stood over me.

"Milarepa, my friend," he said sweetly.

Again, I closed my eyes and opened them. "Thither," I answered weakly, "is it really you?"

The young man smiled and nodded. "Indeed, it is," he said, studying me.

I drew in a deep breath, closing and opening my eyes again. The pain prevented me from speaking.

"You will be all right," Thither said. "It may take some time for you to heal, but you will be all right." He hesitated, looking at me affectionately.

"Am I in Nar?" I asked with some difficulty.

Thither nodded. "You were brought here by two sisters who found you lying at the foot of the mountain," he said. "You are in the guru Marpa's house. Marpa's wife Nadar has been nursing you."

The women on the road had heard me cry out, after all.

"Rest now," Thither said. "When you are ready, you will rise, but do not try to do so until you are ready."

I gratefully closed my eyes and quickly slipped back into sleep.

After some time, I awoke again. The room was empty, and I remained still a moment, listening to the sounds of chickens cackling outside the window. Slowly, and with great discomfort, I sat up and then stood, remembering Thither and Nadar, and seeing that they had left me a fresh change of clothes, I put them on. There was also a bowl of tsamba and a cup of buttered tea, which, although no longer hot, was still warm and soothing to my throat. When I had finished eating and drinking, I felt stronger and went outside.

At first, I saw no one and stood looking at the well-built structure fashioned out of native stone. There was a small garden outside the main door and, off to the side, was a chicken pen. I paused and listened to their cackle, noting the mocking quality of the sound, and then became aware of someone coming out of the chicken house. It was Nadar.

"You look much better now," she called encouragingly, crossing the chicken yard and stepping outside. "Did you eat?"

I told her that I had and thanked her.

"Thither is with Marpa," Nadar said, as though she anticipated the question that was rising in me.

"Which way did they go?" I asked.

Nadar pointed to a stand of trees in the distance, saying that I should follow the path next to the stream.

I thanked her and went on my way. I hadn't gone far when I came to a farmer, plowing a field. I called out to him and asked him if he had seen Thither and Marpa. He said that he had. I then asked which way they had gone. He said that he wasn't sure which way Thither had gone, but that he knew where Marpa was. I asked him to tell me.

"What do you want to know for?" the farmer asked, turning to face me. He was a giant of a man, a good head taller than myself, and had keen, dark eyes. The moment my eyes caught his I was thrilled by a feeling of inexpressibly ecstatic bliss. I lost all consciousness of my surroundings. Finally, I returned to my senses and answered that I wished to thank the guru for the use of his house during my recuperation from a journey through the mountains.

The farmer continued to eye me. I avoided looking into his eyes. "It seems your journey was no mere journey," he said.

I lowered my eyes, struck by the sudden memory of the great Lama Yungtun-Trogyal. Uneasily, I asked, "Which way did you see Marpa go?"

The farmer seemed not to hear my question. "You don't remember me, do you?" He asked, a faint smile appearing on his lips.

Uncertain, I didn't answer.

"I once told you of a shortcut into Tsang," he said. "And we met before that, as well...at a party near your village."

I looked at the man, suddenly remembering him and my mother's wrath following our good time together. She had beat me and sent me to find the black magician.

The man laughed at my surprise. "And you are here to find the guru," he said seriously.

"Yes," I answered, with sudden conviction in my voice. "I am here to find the guru."

"I hear he's a tough old bird," the man said, eyeing me.

"It may take a tough old bird to teach the likes of me," I answered.

The farmer smiled, glancing down at his plow and beast and then at me again. "I'd be glad to get the guru for you, but I have to finish my work here. See," he said, pointing to a far corner of the field, "there is still a bit more work to be done."

My eyes followed the direction the farmer had been pointing. It was more than a corner of the field that still required plowing, more like half of it. It would take a few hours to finish. "I'll go look around," I said, "perhaps someone else can tell me where to find Marpa."

"I doubt it," the farmer said. "Most people hereabouts won't discuss the guru with a stranger." He paused. "But you're not a stranger to me, so I'll arrange the meeting."

"That's very kind," I said, motioning to the unplowed field, "but I can see that you are very busy."

"Nonsense," the farmer said, "I'll tell you what....you work the plow while I go and arrange the meeting with Marpa." He paused, staring at me. "Is that fair enough?" he asked.

I hesitated, unsure if I had the strength or the inclination for the work.

"Come now, you do want to meet the guru, don't you?" the farmer asked. "It shouldn't take me long to arrange the meeting for you. You would only have to do as much of the plowing as it takes me time to arrange it. I will be pleased to be of service to you."

I declined, saying that I could wait, that I would meet the guru later at his house.

"You could do that," the farmer agreed, eyeing me, "but when one is given the opportunity of meeting the guru and turns it down, the opportunity may not come again so soon. For instance, you say you have been staying at the guru's house, and yet you have never seen him."

What the farmer said was true, and, for some reason I didn't understand, I felt compelled to agree, although I made it plain that I would only do the farmer's plowing until his return. The farmer agreed, and turning over the plow and ox reins, he walked off to find Marpa.

Cracking the reins, I prodded the heavy animal to move. I had difficulty holding the tiller to the soil, at first, but then, after awhile, I found that if I leaned on it in a certain way and used my weight as leverage, the tiller cut into the soil like the edge of a sharp knife. As it sliced into the soil, I pushed the opposite way on the handle and the pull of the ox upturned the soil. As I caught onto it, the task became suddenly pleasurable, stretching the sore muscles in my arms, legs, back, and chest in a way that actually relieved the stiffness and pain I had accumulated in the mountains.

I had just finished the job, removed the harness from my shoulders, and leaned the tiller against a tree on the far end of the field, when Thither appeared. He called out, waving his arms to get my attention. I dropped the ox reins, patted the beast, and started towards him.

Thither smiled as I approached. "I see you are suddenly strong again," he said cheerfully.

I raised my arms, flexing my muscles. Then I told him the story of the farmer and how he had gotten me to work for him. When I had finished, I looked around, as though expecting to see him, and laughed. "He never came back," I said.

"He sent me to get you," Thither answered. He was suddenly serious and his expression struck me as odd. I had the peculiar feeling that I was moving about in a dream again, but I tried to ignore it. "Then I am to meet Marpa," I said.

Thither did not speak, but stood gazing at me. His eyes were soft but filled with questions.

I shook my head. "Please, my friend, don't ask me anything now."

Thither nodded that he understood. "All right," he said, "then let us go and find the farmer."

He led the way back to the house where I had slept. The chickens cackled in the yard, as if to remind me that I was a humorous sight, and scurried out of the way. I followed Thither into the stone house and through the kitchen where Nadar was working. She paused to look up at me as we passed, putting her finger to her lips. I sensed she was concerned for me. Thither led me past the room where I had slept and down a flight of steps, which led to a room beneath the surface of the ground. The room was aglow with lamps, and at the far end, a man sat on two thicknesses of cushions with a carpet over them. Although his head was lowered, his huge body dominated the room. Thither paused, motioning to me to go ahead of him.

I moved slowly toward the man. As the great head lifted and looked full upon me, I stopped, recognizing the man who had had me plow his field. Staring at him, I saw that, although he had taken some pains to wipe himself clean, his brow and the corners of his nose still bore some traces of dust.

"I am Marpa," the man said good-naturedly, "although I can see that you may take some convincing of the fact."

I quickly turned to face Thither, who was bowing low behind me. My body began to tremble involuntarily, and I wondered if the horrible dreams were beginning again. I thought of the mountains and the phantom images that had followed me and then, gradually, the images sifted through me, like sand through a net, and faded. They yielded to the memory of a cart driver from Nar who had suggested the forest route to Tsang and to meeting the farmer plowing his field. I recalled the ecstacy that had filled me as I had gazed into his eyes.

I boldly raised my eyes to the guru. "Why is it that I never knew you until now?" I asked.

Marpa's expression was soft and kind when he answered. "Because, until now, you were not ready."

I stared at the guru, unable to think of anything to say. I could feel his eyes resting on me in a kindly way. I considered the feelings I had had when I believed my existence to be a dream, and I asked him if our meeting was a part of that dreamstate.

Marpa gazed at me with his deep, dark eyes and, in them, I saw tiny images of myself. In a quiet voice, he asked, "Was it a dream when I challenged you to a drinking bout at the fateful feast? Was it a dream when I told you of the forest route to Tsang? Were you dreaming that your muscles pulled at my plow? Are you dreaming that you, a great sorcerer, are standing before me now?"

I was stunned by his questions, particularly his reference to my being a great sorcerer.

"Great Sorcerer," Marpa said, "did they teach you nothing at the Lama Yungtun-Trogyal's monastery?"

I gazed at the man, confused and suddenly dizzy, filled with an echo of the black magician's name. After a moment, I lowered my head and tried to compose myself.

"Sit and tell me of your misdeeds," Marpa said kindly.

I sat and slowly raised my head again, trying to focus my eyes on the guru's face, but a terrible pain began to throb inside my chest and my ears pounded. Tears overflowed my eyes and streamed down my cheeks. I wept uncontrollably until gradually I gained control of myself again. I told the guru of my journey through the mountains, of stripping myself of the black magician's robe and walking naked in an effort to forget what I had done, but that the fiends of my living dreams still tormented me. Between sobs, I described what I had seen in my dreams—the destruction of my village and my mother's corpse—and I also related the threats from the black magician that I was doomed and cursed. Finally, I told how, when high in the mountains, I remembered Thither's story of Nar where the guru Marpa lived and that I had come here as my last chance for survival.

I paused, gazing at the guru, pleading with my eyes for help. I said that I would do anything that the guru asked of me in exchange.

Marpa shifted his large body on the floor opposite me and told me to begin again, saying that the story I told was incomplete and disjointed.

At a motion from Marpa, Thither sat down next to me. I felt strengthened by his presence and sat straighter, controlling the rush of emotion that was filling me. I lifted my head and raised my eyes to meet the Lama's gaze and began speaking carefully, choosing my words, knowing that Marpa was listening closely. I sensed that the Lama listened, not only to my words but to my heart, his quick eyes reaching into me. I told him my story from the beginning: how my mother had threatened suicide if I failed my mission and how, even after my succeeding, she had killed herself. I also told how I had found her corpse. I wept as I told the story, pausing occasionally to compose myself. I even told the Lama of my beloved Zesay, my sister Peta, and Thither. When I finished some hours later, I waited for the Lama to speak.

"Very well," Marpa said, drawing in a long breath, "I will help you, but I cannot give you all that you ask. I cannot give you food, clothing, and instruction. You will have to choose. Either I will provide you with food and clothing, and you will find instruction elsewhere, or I will give you instruction, and you can find food and clothing elsewhere. It is your choice."

I did not hesitate. "I have come to you to learn," I said. "I will find my clothing and food elsewhere."

Marpa's eyes narrowed and he tilted his head to one side. "I am skeptical about your nature," he said. "If I give you the truth you seek, it will be in reward for your perseverance to gain it. Your personal supply of energy will determine whether or not you will attain the grand liberation."

A slow chill rippled through me. I nodded that I understood and was grateful, but I knew that the great Lama would challenge me in a way so fierce that I could not imagine it.

"You will sleep and eat here tonight," Marpa said, rising to his feet. Thither and I stood up, as well. Marpa's great body had a height and majesty to it that made me feel suddenly humbled. "In the morning," Marpa said again, "you must leave and earn your food."

Marpa's wife Nadar waited in the outer room. She smiled pleasantly when she saw me coming through the doorway, as though she knew what to expect. Then she quickly led me into the kitchen where she placed a large bowl of tsamba in front of me.

I hesitated, turning to see if Thither was to join me, but he was not there.

Nadar put her hand on my shoulder. "You must eat," she said gently.

I looked up at her with dazed eyes.

"You must eat," she said again.

Obediently, I dipped my fingers into the bowl and lifted the doughy tsamba to my lips. I looked at it a moment and then ate, the pasty gruel sticking to the roof of my mouth.

"If I give you the truth you seek,
it will be in reward
for your perseverance to gain it."

CHAPTER ELEVEN

THE PENANCE
BEGINS

I opened my eyes. Scenes from memory overlapped the smooth, grey dirt ceiling above me and, for a moment, I was not sure where I was. The ceiling could have been one in the monastery and, while images of the black magician, Narquin, and Steita loomed overhead, the guru Marpa was superimposed over them. As though in the distance, the Lama Yungtun-Trogyal was calling out to me, demanding that I return to the monastery. Nearer was the guru Marpa, telling me that he would not offer food and clothing as well as spiritual instruction, saying that I would have to choose.

I sat up on my bed. The grey fog of the black magician's voice faded further and further into the distance. The choice was clear. I would heal the wounds of spirit and survive. I slowly rose to my feet, stretching to ease the stiff, sore feeling from my body, and then lifted the dried grass curtain from the doorway and stepped through it into the kitchen.

I looked about, piecing together memories of my meal there, and recalled the kindly manner of Marpa's wife, and then crossed the kitchen to another door and stepped outside.

The day was warm and clear with a bright, mid-day sun overhead. The air was fresh-scented and mellow, touched with a dreamy, iridescent quality. As though moving about in a dream, I went to the well, drew a bucket of water, and doused myself with it. I rubbed the cool liquid through my hair and, smoothing it, I drew it back and twisted it into a knot at the back of my head. As I was doing this, I noticed a basket carelessly resting against a tree. When I finished with my hair, I went over to it and picked it up. I dusted the dirt from it and reshaped the center into a bowl with my hands, quickly deciding that the basket had been discarded and was mine to use as a receptacle for alms. Then I looked up, my attention drawn to the huge, barren mountains towering above the valley. Their greyish countenance loomed upward as a fortress. Looking at them, I spotted a section of the narrow trail as it disappeared behind the jagged formations. I shivered, remembering that just a short time ago, I had roamed those mountains naked, lost, and tormented by hideous dream-like demons.

Gazing at the jagged terrain, remembering, it occurred to me that memories were like dreams; that the nature of a memory and the nature of a dream was the same. They were both visions in imagination. The dream and the memory were both mental images, the difference being that the dream was a series of passing images, while the memory was an image solidified. What then was truly a dream? It was sleeping. It was daydreaming. But moreover, if indeed, dreams were a result of images passing through the mind, then life itself was a dream, a waking dream, filled with the same symbolic dramas as those experienced in sleep or trance.

I slowly turned and looked about Marpa's yard. If I had been dreaming, if I was dreaming still—the well, the chickens, and the yak tied to a tree were all properties of the dream. They were real, and yet their presence produced images in my mind, units of my imagination, united with the vision and perception of what I saw.

I was both hopeful and astounded by the revelation, and I considered that, if my mind suddenly went still and I imagined nothing, the dream would end. What would the dreamless state be like? Would I awaken to find myself in a totally different place, another direction, and clutching the alms basket to my breast, I turned and hurried down the valley road in search of food.

I stopped at the first house I saw. A woman was outside, kneading tsamba on a slab of clean rock. She did not look up as I approached, although I sensed that she was aware of me. I waited politely to be recognized.

"Who are you?" the woman asked finally, giving me a quick sideways glance.

"I am Milarepa, student of Marpa the translator," I answered politely.

The woman broke off a section of dough and handed it to me without looking at me. "It is all I can spare," she said brusquely.

"Thank you," I said, "but I would like to repay you for your kindness."

The women stopped kneading and turned to me. She appeared older than I had believed. "What do you have in mind?" she asked.

"To do some work for you," I answered politely.

The woman nodded approvingly, studying me in a peculiar way. "You don't look very strong," she said finally.

"But I am strong," I said reassuringly.

The woman motioned to a small herd of yaks in a pen next to the house. "Collect the yak droppings and put them in the fire pile," she instructed. "But first, you must eat your tsamba."

I broke off half of the tsamba she had given me. I ate it and placed the other half in the alms basket I was carrying as the woman watched. Then I hurried off to the pen on the side of her house and collected all of the dung dropped by her yaks and placed it in the fire pile next to the woman's cooking pit. While I was working, I remembered my recognition that life was a dream, and I viewed this moment as part of that dream, that the farm woman, her home, and livestock were not only a part of my dream, but that I was a part of her dream, as well. The idea fascinated me, although I was unable to grasp the meaning of it. When I had finished, I went to the woman, thanked her again and set out for the next house.

At the next farm, I found a man curing meat at the rear of his house. The succulent aroma immediately attracted my attention, and I hurried to him, holding my basket humbly before me.

The man turned abruptly and stared first at me then at the basket. "You are hungry?" the man asked.

"Yes, please," I answered politely, my begging basket in front of me.

"And why should I give you food?" the man asked.

I hesitated and, seeing the man as an image in a dream, the question seemed logical. I tried to think of a logical answer. "Because I have no meat and I would like some," I answered finally.

"You already have some tsamba, I see," the man added, motioning with a tilt of his head to the tsamba in my basket. "Isn't it good enough for you?"

"Oh, yes," I answered quickly, "but what is in the basket is half of what a woman at a nearby house gave me in exchange for collecting her yak dung," I said.

"I suppose you ate the other half," the man said.

"Yes."

"And the half you have in there?" he asked, pointing to the tsamba.

"This is for my guru," I said. "My guru is Marpa the translator."

The man seemed disturbed and quickly handed over a large piece of dried meat and then waved me away.

"What may I do for you in exchange?" I asked, hesitating.

"You may leave me alone," the man said without looking at me.

I did not know what to say, but I did not want to take anything from the man without doing something for him in return. It was a principle my beloved Zesay had taught me and one that I felt was most agreeable. I was sure that, had my father lived, it would have been a principle he would have lived by, even though my mother had not.

"You can leave me alone," the man said, coolly facing me.

I was surprised and lowered my eyes.

The man sucked a breath of air through his teeth. "If I allow you to work for me, then you will consider the alms as wages, and I did not wish to hire your services in the first place," the man answered. "Now go, beggar, and leave me alone."

I felt truly humbled. As the son of a nobleman, although penniless, in my village people's eyes, I was considered above the ordinary. Now, suddenly, this man had stripped that self-esteem from me, and I understood what real poverty must be like. The man believed me to be a pest, scavenging for food, and I was too weak from my adventures to pretend otherwise.

"Be gone with you," the man said again, waving his hand in a backward motion to indicate that I was to leave at once.

I handed the man back his meat and quickly turned and hurried off his land.

I walked for a long time, thinking about the two householders I had visited and my theory of living dreams. The woman who had given me tsamba, although kind, had looked at me in much the same way as the farmer had. She, too, had seen me as a person in need although, when I had offered to repay her with work, her attitude toward me changed. It seemed that she had allowed me to influence her image of me. Her image of me was how she saw me in her imagination, her dream life. The farmer, on the other hand, seemed not to have an image of me as an individual at all. To him, I was a beggar, a person who intruded on the livelihood of others without invitation to do so. His imagination, his dream world, was fixed on the collective image and he was not easily influenced. His living dream was rigid. I was fascinated by the thought that imagination was THE source of power behind the dreams.

As I walked slowly, thinking about the waking state of dreams, a man riding a yak came up alongside me. He drew his beast to an abrupt halt and, without comment, he reached into the bundles on the back of the animal, withdrew a sack of barley, and handed it down to me. It all happened so suddenly that I could think of nothing to say, and before I could recover, the man on yak-back rode away and left me there, holding the sack of barley. Forgetting myself, happy for the gift, I excitedly turned around and hurried back to Marpa's house.

Marpa was standing in the doorway when I returned.

I quickly placed the alms at the guru's feet and stepped back.

"What is this?" Marpa suddenly roared, kicking the sack of barley meal and begging basket to one side.

I was visibly shaken by the guru's reaction. "A gift for your household, my guru," I answered.

Marpa looked deeply into my eyes and, for a moment, although terrified, I was filled with the deep and sudden ecstasy that I had felt when I first met the Lama in the fields.

"Do you think you can buy me?" Marpa asked coolly.

"It was not my intention," I answered, humbled by the fact

that, in truth, I was making an offering to the Lama in exchange for instruction. I thought of my dream discoveries and wished that I could discuss them with him, but the guru did not seem open to discussion. I lowered my eyes to hide from the guru's gaze.

"What is it you have discovered?" Marpa asked, eyeing me. The guru knew.

Thoughts about my dream revelations rushed forward and I was suddenly confused as to where to begin. "Life is a dream," I said finally.

Marpa stared at me for a long while without speaking. Finally he said, "If you wish my instruction, you will have to do everything I say without question."

"I will," I said hopefully, looking up in answer to the guru's challenge. I was filled with expectancy about what he might say about the dream.

Marpa continued to look deeply into me and then smiled. "But, of course," he said lightly, "you are a great sorcerer. You do know about following instructions, do you not?"

I did not know what to say and lowered my eyes. Being called a great sorcerer was not meant to be a compliment. The fact that I had learned to follow instructions had been demonstrated by the power I had displayed in destroying my enemies, and while I did not truly understand how I had used the power, the fact remained that I had used it and that power now cursed me. I wondered if Marpa had misunderstood me or had not heard me at all when I told him of my revelation that life was a dream.

"Well, great sorcerer?" Marpa asked again.

"Life is a dream," I said again.

Marpa's eyes narrowed, studying me. "Is that your answer?" he asked coolly.

He had not misunderstood me after all. I was disappointed. "I am grateful that you will teach me," I said humbly, "and I will do whatever it is that you tell me to do."

Marpa smiled again. "Good," he said. "I have a task for you." He pointed to a hill behind his home. "We will go there and I will show you what I want you to do."

As we walked in silence, Marpa in the lead, I thought again of telling the guru my thoughts on the imagination and how the images produced by it affected dreams, but everytime I touched the subject, the guru quickened his pace and I would have to hurry to catch up. Finally, we reached the top of the hill and stopped walking. I looked around. It was a pretty spot, almost directly above Marpa's house. I could see Nadar in the yard, feeding the chickens. Thither was there with her, sweeping the chicken droppings to a manure pile off to the side of the yard.

A sound from Marpa shifted my attention to the hilltop again. He had moved his great body and was pointing to the ground. It was covered with rock, stones of all sizes, including many large ones. A few sprigs of grass, catsclaw, and indigo managed to sprout between the stones. Off to the left was a single bodhi tree. I turned to face the guru who was watching me.

"It's a beautiful tree, is it not?" Marpa asked.

I nodded, uneasily, I knew that I had not been led there to admire a tree.

"And look at the view from up here," Marpa said, motioning with a sweep of his hand. "One can see for miles. Isn't it beautiful?"

"Yes," I said, gazing down at Marpa's house. Thither was following Nadar across the yard. I turned and looked at the guru again.

Marpa turned and slowly began to walk across the rugged terrain. When he had reached the tree, he patted it affectionately and turned to me. "Oh, great and powerful sorcerer," Marpa said in a voice that pretended to be sincere, "if you wish my instruction, you will have to first prove your loyalty to me."

"I will do anything you ask," I answered, wishing that he would not call me sorcerer. I knew he used the word mockingly to humble me for my evil deeds.

"I have thought a great deal about your training, great sorcerer," Marpa said, "and I believe that I have found the best task for you." He paused, staring at me, gazing into me in such a way that I felt his eyes touch a secret part of me. It was thrilling.

"Anything you ask," I said again, as though speaking to him from a distance. It was the dream feeling but somehow different from the dream feelings I had had before.

"As you can see, there is plenty of stone here," Marpa said, turning and looking about the hilltop. Then he turned back to me.

"Milarepa, I want you to build me a house."

I thought I had misunderstood the guru and so I hesitated, listening intensely, following the motions of his hands with my eyes.

"The house should be placed near the tree so that the branches provide shade for a hot summer's day, but not so near as to threaten the growth of the tree." Marpa paused, moving away from the tree, counting his steps as he moved, finally stopping and planting his feet firmly in a spot some twenty paces away. "Here," he said. "This will do nicely." He reached down and picked up a large stone and placed it in front of his foot. "Build the house here." He paused again, barely looking at me before he went on." Build the house two stories high. When you have finished, I will teach you what you wish to know." He stopped and turned suddenly.

I was wide-eyed, staring at the building site Marpa had designated. I had expected unusual treatment from this guru, but I had not expected to build him a house in exchange for his knowledge. I had never built a house and wasn't sure that I knew how to begin. I wondered if Thither had undergone such treatment when he had first come to the guru.

"Great sorcerer, I see that you hesitate," Marpa said seriously. "Is it because you lack the power to accomplish a task with your hands?"

I stared at the guru Marpa, trying to understand the purpose of the task he requested. Was it purely to mock me, or was he testing me to see if I could take his direction? I tried to collect myself, to appear humble and anxious, but instead, a slow anger was rising in me and I could not entirely hide it. "I am not a great sorcerer," I said in a cool voice, "but I will do as you ask, and then I will claim my reward."

Marpa smiled.

"You will instruct me as promised," I said, pressing for a commitment.

"Indeed, I will, great sorcerer," Marpa said. "Indeed, I will." His great head lifted and he cast a sideways glance at me. "Build the house I request, and I will teach you." Marpa turned and, leaving me behind, he started down the hill.

I had felt that I was to stay and begin work, but how could I work when I had to beg my food? Was he trying to humiliate me, believing that I would fail and return to the black magician's monastery, or did he merely think me a fool? "Wait!" I shouted after him.

Marpa stopped but did not turn around.

"Am I to stay and build the house now?" I called out. "If you wish my instruction," Marpa said in an even voice. "If you do not want it, then do not build the house."

"But how am I to build a house and still have time to beg for food?" I asked

"That is no concern of mine," the guru answered, with his back to me.

"Are you to leave me here with nothing?" I shouted. I was suddenly angry and I could not control it.

"It is not my place to care for your body," Marpa said, his back still to me. "We agreed that you would feed and clothe yourself. I will care only for your spiritual needs."

"If I am to do your work then you must help me," I yelled.

"The work I give you is part of your instruction," Marpa answered.

I was fuming, wishing to curse at the guru, but I was afraid he would send me away. "But I must eat to work," I yelled instead. "Can you not at least offer me the return of the food I have given you? You rejected it anyway."

Marpa slowly turned around, facing me. "Do as you like," he said kindly. "You may take it. The sack of barley grain lies where you left it. I have no need of your gifts."

The guru's expression was one of pity, and I could not help but feel angered by the humility I felt. I lowered my head, staring blankly at the large, grey rock at my feet.

Marpa turned away again and continued down the hill. I looked after him. Feelings of shame and worthlessness rubbed at me, churning my anger into hatred. I wanted to study with the guru, and yet, I hated him for what he made me feel in his presence.

Later that day, I returned to the guru's house to collect the sack of barley meal I had left outside his door. It was untouched in exactly the same position as the great Marpa's foot had placed it. I picked it up and slung it high on my shoulder. Bruises from my climb over the mountains throbbed at the gesture and, for an instant, I recalled the unnatural feelings that I had had.

I hesitated, hoping to speak with Thither, but I saw no one. As I looked about, I fantasized telling Thither about Marpa's unreasonable request that I build him a house and imagined Thither's shocked expression. Perhaps Thither had even discovered Marpa to be an imposter and had left to find another guru. I could imagine him telling me that Marpa had nothing to teach, that the guru needed a new house and found in me an easy prey to build it.

I lingered, looking at Marpa's house, and wondered if everyone was inside the house, looking out, watching me. I considered that they had been instructed to ignore my presence, to peek out at me only from the interior shadows. I stared at the house as if staring back at them. The kitchen window was open, and as I stood examining the dark opening from a distance, I expected to see some sort of movement, but there was none.

Would no one offer me water or beer to take with me? Was I meant to spend all of my time begging so that I would have little time to build the house Marpa requested? Did Marpa mean to trick me so that I would never finish, never be accepted to his instruction?

I turned and went to Marpa's household well, which was situated in the center of the yard, but upon reaching it, I found I could not turn the handle and raise the bucket with the sack of grain on my shoulder. Yet, if I put the sack down, I was not sure I could manage to pick it up again and still manage the water. I looked into the water well, staring into it for a long moment, spitting and cursing into it, then turned away, carrying my sack of grain back up the hill behind Marpa's house.

When I arrived there, to my surprise, I found Marpa standing angrily, his feet spread apart, his hands tightly rolled into fists that rested on his hips. He was like an angry giant standing broad-legged under the tree.

I hesitated, somewhat frightened of him.

"How dare you curse my well," Marpa growled. "Great sorcerer or not, I will separate your body from your limbs and hang the pieces of you on the bodhi tree if you ever utter a curse near my home again."

Shaken by the guru's anger, I dropped the grain. It hit the rocky ground with a thud, ripping open and spilling in all directions. It was true that I had cursed the Lama's well, but not with any particular intention. It was simply a curse that I had said and then dismissed immediately after having spoken it.

"Did the Lama Yungtun-Trogyal tell you what could happen if you did not immediately return to his monastery after your misdeeds?" Marpa snapped.

I stood wide-eyed, staring at the guru, certain that I had not mentioned the Lama Yungtun-Trogyal's warning. But it was true, the black magician had cautioned me, saying that if I did not return to the monastery, I could effect a curse that would doom me throughout eternity.

"You have the power, great sorcerer," Marpa said, his voice thundering in the open air. "Did you think that one with power can whisper casual curses and have them ignored by the lords of the universe?"

"I did not think," I said humbly, not at all sure that I knew what Marpa meant. I did not feel that I had any power.

"You did not think!" Marpa said, repeating me. "You must never utter another word without careful thought about its consequences. Better yet, you must not think. Your thoughts are stinking!" He paused, narrowing his big eyes at me. "You worm! You scum! Murderer! You have maimed others in your ignorance! You have destroyed life, and now you tell me that you did not know what you were doing!"

As though in a dream, I was suddenly outside of my body, looking at myself. I saw myself trembling, a weak pitiful form, doubling over and falling to the ground before the form of Marpa the translator.

"Rise to your feet," Marpa demanded.

I crawled to my knees and slowly rose to my feet. I watched myself, and the part of me that was watching moved away and stood next to Marpa. I was also my own accuser.

Marpa reached down to the base of the tree and brought forth a large bucket. "Here is the water that you cursed," he said, holding it out to me. "It is yours to drink. It may poison you and the poison may kill you. If you die, you do so at your own hand, by your own curse. If you do not die, you will build the house I instructed you to build and, in return, I will reveal to you the secrets of divinity."

I remembered that I had not seen Thither but could not bring myself to ask. Instead, I stood quite still, aware that a part of myself stood strong and firm next to Marpa while the other part swayed pitifully before him. I had the odd sensation that I was deep in sleep on the very brink of awakening. Marpa's gaze held me, as though his gaze alone was the force that kept me on my feet. I tried to keep Marpa in focus, but whenever it seemed that I could see him clearly, I could also see myself standing next to him. I took the pail of water and, as Marpa had instructed me to do, lifted it to my lips and drank. After several deep swallows, I lowered the bucket again and put it on the ground between us. When next I looked up, Marpa was gone. The vision of myself next to Marpa was also gone.

The days passed slowly. Because I felt weak and tired, I never left the hill. The only liquid I had to drink was that that Marpa had brought me from the well. I was certain that it was poisoned, yet I drank it. With every swallow, my stomach revolted in tight pains, and even after the pains lessened, I constantly felt nauseous. I chewed on the barley grain, which sometimes helped. Whenever the pain in my stomach relaxed, I gathered stones and stacked them according to size. Mostly I gathered small stones, which were not such a drain on my strength but, even then, I rested more than I worked. It seemed that I would never get well and strong again. I even considered that I might die.

As I moved about the hill, I frequently thought of the time in the Lama Yungtun-Trogyal's monastery when I had discovered the kitchen monks tainting the food that was to be served to me. It seemed that there was some connection between that incident and my own curse over Marpa's water supply and the fact that I was sick from it.

My vision blurred and I sat down, slipping into the crevice between two fair-sized rocks and staring blankly into space. I did not try to move. Specks of light danced before my eyes, and when I tried to narrow my focus, the images before me multiplied. Sometimes I saw two of everything and sometimes more. I knew that the poisoned water had saturated my system and that my curse was about to consume me. Until now, I had tried to fight death by working. It was not that I was afraid to die, but that I had hoped to achieve a little quality in the passing. I had hoped to free myself from the doom that had been forecast for me by the black magician, to lift my spirit above it, but I realized now that I was beyond redemption.

I closed my eyes and drew in a slow, painful breath. The nearness of death seemed almost sweet to me. My thoughts called to it, begging it to come nearer, to take me quickly. Then suddenly, I felt a touch and, feeling that my prayer had been answered, I opened my eyes to meet it.

"Relax, my friend," a gentle voice said. Someone's firm grip lifted me. I turned my head and saw that Thither had cradled me in his arms. "Nadar, give Milarepa a drink of the beer," Thither said softly.

I gazed up at the blurred image of Thither. Nadar was next to him, holding a jar of thick, yellow liquid. She raised it to my lips and told me to drink.

"Take more," Thither prodded. "Milarepa, you must drink as much as you can."

Drawn by the insistence of Thither's voice, I obediently sipped the liquid.

"Poor devil," Nadar said, studying my pitiful face. "If he dies, I will never forgive my husband."

"He will not die," Thither said with certainty. "Marpa has said that he will live."

"No thanks to him," Nadar said angrily. "Oh, poor boy."

I gazed at her kind face but was unable to focus upon it. Finally, I gave up and closed my eyes, while continuing to sip the sweet chang beer until I blacked out.

I opened my eyes and looked above me into the limbs of a tree. The heart-shaped bodhi leaves danced on the breeze-blown branches. I became aware that my body was stretched out flat beneath the tree and a wool fleece, which someone had placed upon me to protect me from the cold, covered me. I slowly moved my hands and legs beneath the warm blanket and sat up.

Looking about, I saw no one. I was alone on the hilltop. I recalled that Thither had been there, and that Marpa's wife Nadar had fed me chang beer.

After a time, I pushed aside the wool fleece and rose to my feet. Next to the tree, where I had been sleeping, were several small pouches. I reached down and opened them to find a plentiful supply of a variety of foods, including meat and tsamba. Also on the ground were a number of containers of beer. I opened one of the jars and drank before hungrily filling myself on the food, and then I drank again. When I was satisfied, I stretched and walked slowly across the terrain. I had no idea how long I had been asleep but my body felt strong and renewed with life. I had not died after all. I had been given another chance, although I knew that my life would now be much different than it had been. I would guard my speech and thoughts no matter how alone and unheard I thought my words would be. I would never again dare to curse anything, knowing that if I did, I might forfeit my life.

The discovery gave me a feeling of peculiar strength, I felt suddenly exhilarated and filled with insight into a part of life I had never before known existed, and yet I knew with great certainty that it did exist. I suddenly saw that every time in my life that I had cursed something, I had spread the poison of that curse. Sometimes, I had hurt others with it and always, unknowingly, I had hurt myself. Perhaps in my ignorance, I hadn't recognized the pain I had inflicted on others or why I suddenly met with difficulties and injury, but the truth was that I was responsible. My curses had moved out in a circle, affecting others and returning to me in disguise. It seemed that Marpa, in a most subtle fashion, had already taught me a great principle of life and, although I knew that I only partially understood it, the recognition filled me with joy.

I quickly looked around. The small pile of stones that I had collected during my illness seemed meager for the task ahead. I went to the spot some twenty paces from the tree that Marpa had marked as a corner of the house, studied it a moment and then spotted a nearby stone that would fit it. It was a large stone, round on the sides and flat on top and it was perfectly balanced for setting other stones next to it. I lifted it, aware that the pull on my muscles felt good, and I carefully positioned it where I believed Marpa would want it to be. Then I placed another and another, noticing how each fit perfectly with the next, and I began to talk to Marpa in my thoughts, telling him of the joy I was feeling at carrying out the task for him. Indeed, it was as if Marpa was there, encouraging me, pointing out the exact stone to lay next. Marpa, in thought, was my constant companion and, in thought, all fear that I had had of him disappeared. The guru became more than a companion, he became a friend. As the days passed, my thoughts poured out to him, trusting him and loving him. I would go to sleep at night, knowing that the guru's presence protected me, and when I awakened in the morning, a fresh supply of food reinforced this confidence.

It did not take long, working steadily day after day, before Marpa's house was very nearly built. On the day that I thought I would finish, Marpa paid me a visit. I had not seen him climb the summit, although I had been thinking of him particularly strongly that day, and when I looked up from my work, the guru was there.

Marpa stood with his hands behind his back, looking up at the impressive two-story structure. Then he walked around it, carefully studying every line and detail, viewing its straightness first from one angle and then another.

I had paused in my work, watching the guru with satisfaction, waiting for him to speak.

Marpa finally came and stood next to me, motioning toward the structure with outstretched hands. "It is a work of art," he said finally.

I smiled, modestly keeping my silence.

"I had no idea that you could build such a perfect house," Marpa said, complimenting me.

"It is because you were with me, my guru," I said humbly. "You helped me choose each stone. It made the building an easy task instead of an impossible one."

Marpa was silent for what seemed a long while. "I am pleased you have such confidence in your guru," he said, "especially since it is your guru's sad task to tell you that his brother has claimed this site for his own. He said that I may not build here."

I was shocked and turned to stare at Marpa. "But the house is nearly finished," I cried.

Marpa nodded sadly. "I can see," he said, "but what am I to do? My brother says that I was mistaken; that this land does not belong to my wife and me and that our house cannot be built here."

I forced myself to ask, "What will we do, my guru?"

"I do not like to ask it of you, Milarepa, but I must," Marpa said, pausing to study me. "It was our agreement that you would build me a house on my own land in exchange for the secrets of divinity. As you can see, the house you have built, while perfectly done, is not on my land. My land is over there." Marpa paused, pointing to the hill next to the one we were standing upon. "But surely, with the love and confidence you have found with me as your guru, you will have no trouble in tearing this house down and building over there."

I was too astounded to speak. I stared first at Marpa, then at the opposite hill, and then at Marpa again. Had the guru tricked me? Was he treating me in this manner because he did not wish to teach me as promised, or was it possible that the guru was not a guru at all and had nothing to teach? I was seized with doubts.

"I wish to share the secrets of divinity with you." Marpa said, aware of my sudden inner confusion. "But first, you must do as you are told. Did you forget that you promised to follow my directions without question?" He paused, turning to look at the house. "Of course, if the house you have built has more meaning to you than the secrets of divinity, that is your choice," Marpa said. "You must decide for yourself. Either build the house again on the hill next to this one or leave and seek another guru." Marpa turned to face me. "Great sorcerer, it does not matter to me what you do." Then he turned again and walked back down into the valley leaving me standing there.

*"It occurred to me
that memories were like dreams;
that the nature of a memory
and the nature of a dream was the same.
They were both visions in imagination."*

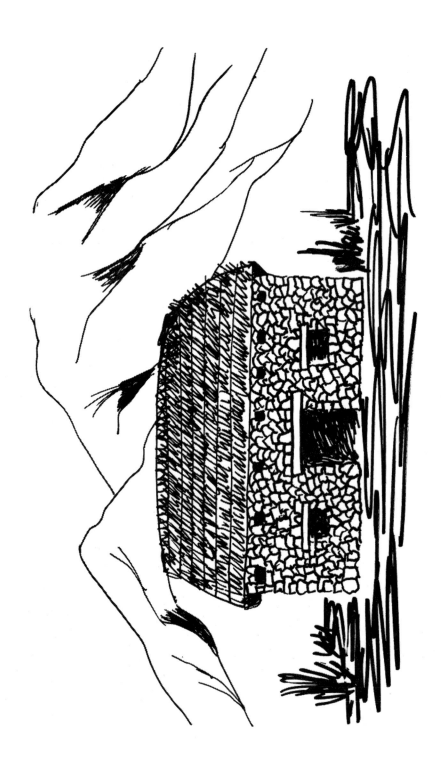

CHAPTER TWELVE
RECOGNITION OF THE DREAM

I stood uneasily on the opposite hillside, looking across to where I had nearly completed Marpa's house. It had taken me nearly two cycles of the moon to build it and merely a few days to tear it down. It seemed ironic to me that it took so long to build something and so short a time to destroy it, comparing the feat of Marpa's house to the events of my short life. And here I was, about to start building again. It all seemed so futile and pointless. Was there any value in the building of another house for Marpa?

I turned and looked about at the new building site. There were fewer stones here and they were smaller than the ones I had used to build the first house. It could take twice as long to build here because of the stones' smaller size. Did Marpa realize this fact?

I reached down and lifted a stone to examine it. It was no bigger than my fist and most of those I saw were about the same size. To build a house the size of the first one would indeed take double the time. I dropped the stone to the ground and kicked it with my foot. Instead of hitting my sandal squarely, the rock made contact with my largest toe and sent a stinging sensation through my foot. Angrily, I reached down, picked up the stone again and flung it wildly. I had turned my head for just a second when I heard a cry and a light thud. Panicked, I ran toward where I had thrown the stone, stopping short at the sight of a crow limping wildly on one leg. My heart sank at the sight. Slowly, I bent down and reached out to the bird, making soft twittering sounds as I beckoned to it. The bird screeched at me as though it understood that I had injured it. With a quick, sudden movement I caught the bird with one hand, and while it flapped its wings wildly, I slowly stroked its black shiny feathers until they surrendered, smooth and relaxed beneath my other hand.

Gradually, I was able to examine the bird's leg, lightly touching it, lifting and turning it until I was satisfied that it was not broken. "You will be all right," I said to the crow, "no thanks to me." I knew I had caused the injury through my mental passion, recalling the awful anger I had felt when I hurled the stone. It was the same frustration that I had felt when I cursed Marpa's water supply. Marpa had cautioned me about the awful power the sorcerer's training had unleashed in me, and I recalled, too, how Narquin had urged me to return immediately to the monastery following the destruction of my enemies in order to avoid further doom. I was again shown the meaning of those warnings.

I gazed sorrowfully at the bird, inwardly apologizing to it. Aloud, I said, "I will remember the pain I caused you and employ the memory as a teacher, so that in the future I will remember and not do it again." Then I opened my hands. The bird turned and looked at me as if it understood and then quickly stretched its wings and flew off. I watched the bird until it was well out of sight. Then, filled with relief and remorse, I slowly turned about, looking in all directions, across the terrain.

This hill had a bodhi tree on it and a few junipers, as well. The trees were slightly smaller than those on the opposite hill, but then, I reasoned that the stones were also smaller and the non-sensical comparison between the two—the trees and the stones—from hill to hill made me laugh at myself. I went over to the tiny grove of trees and, imagining that Marpa was there, I carefully walked twenty paces from them. Then I reached down and formed a stack of the small stones to mark the spot. With the first corner set, I went to the second and marked it off as well, then the third, and finally the last. When all the corners were set, I ran about gathering more stones, making an outline of the house. When this was done, I began to build the foundation. It would be even stronger than the first. By nightfall, the front part of the house had risen to the height of my knees.

I grew stronger by the day, although my body was always sore and cut from working with the abrasive stones. The bending and lifting greatly developed every muscle in my body. My arms and legs became as hard as the stones themselves, and in the wake of my task, the solitude also made me stronger in mind. Because of the quiet direction of my physical energies, I became accustomed to giving attention to the thoughts that were aroused in me. Sometimes, my thoughts raged like those of a madman, while at other times, they were remorseful and self-pitying, and still others were filled with the desire to rise above pettiness. I first discovered this last feeling when I accidentally struck my knee with a stone. I had been setting a corner on one of the interior walls, thinking on the destruction I had caused in my village and wondering if I had indeed killed my aunt and uncle or had merely destroyed their holdings, when my arm bumped a pillar of stones before the mud mortar had set and sent one toppling, catching the sensitive part of my knee. The blow struck me in such a way that I reeled backward in pain and cursed in my customary manner. My immediate thought had been that I wished I could eliminate such cursing from my thoughts and, at the same time, I was aware of another part of myself, wishing to yell out again or to strike back angrily. At that moment, my mind seemed to separate from me, as though it was a separate entity from my real self, and all of its arguments seemed to be tricks. The tricks occurred when my feelings were stirred by some inner imagery. Once the imagery came to mind, it assumed control. The result was either pain or pleasure, and the pleasure, it seemed, often had a way of turning into pain. I reflected back on my life, remembering moments of intense pleasure and how those moments always seemed to be followed by something to upset them. In a way, pain and pleasure seemed to be related, like different branches of the same tree.

It seemed absurd.

I observed myself. A part of me sat angrily, staring at the stone that had struck my knee and wishing to hurl it far from me. Another part watched the angry reaction in myself, remembering how the anger of a hurled stone had injured a bird. I sat there torn between calm and upset, between certainty and uncertainty, realizing that the pull of opposite feelings was creating images in my mind. I was fascinated by the realization and encouraged it to expand in me. I saw myself as a boy, living in Nyang, playing hide and seek with my sister Peta. We were laughing and chasing each other when our aunt came to us with the news that our father had died. In my mind, I saw Peta cover her mouth with her hands in shock, remembering how we had slowly walked hand-in-hand to our father's bedside. At first, we had believed him to be sleeping and not dead at all, but when we touched him, his hands had been stiff and cold. One moment we had been so happy together and then so stricken with unhappiness.

I remembered another time, sitting next to Zesay when we were still quite small. She had said to me that I was a strange but very special boy, and that my life would be very different from most. I believed that she was referring to my family's circumstances, the fact that my father was dead, and that my aunt and uncle had stolen our family fortune, but she had said, no, that my life would be special, that life compensates with opposites, that if one thing was taken from me, it was to make room for something greater.

Images of what I had done to the people of Nyang suddenly returned to me, filling me, and, for a moment, I was wandering naked in the mountains again. Unable to bear it any longer, I descended. The guru had not rescued me from my doom but had merely made it possible to hold it off. He had lifted me from death, so to speak, for as long as I was willing to cooperate. He had given me the task of working through my awful karma.

I picked up a stone and turned it about in my hand, remembering, but not holding tight to any one memory. I was sure that the images passing through my mind were no different than dreams; that the dream-like feelings I had were due to my awareness and recognition of images passing through my mind. I was watching myself and living the dream at the same time.

My previous awareness struck me again. A dream was nothing more than a series of images passing through one's mind. A dream was the result of thought and feeling combined. When thought was blended with feelings, it produced images in mind. These images were dreams. In the waking state, they were daydreams. Asleep, they were sleep dreams. I paused, gazing at the crude foundation of the house I was constructing, aware of myself sitting on the ground next to it, nursing a wounded knee and, gazing about, the peculiar dream-like feeling hovering over me. Even this moment, this present moment, seemed like a dream. It, too, was filled with images, not from inside my mind, reflecting from the past, or wishes for the future, but images in front of me as seen with the physical eyes. Life experiences were dreams, as well.

I was so taken with the idea that I forgot about my knee and rose to my feet, watching myself as though seeing myself rise in a dream. I moved to the stone wall I had been constructing and ran the palm of my hand over its rough surface. Touching it did not prove the wall to be more real than a wall in my sleep dreams. In sleep dreams, too, I touched and saw and heard and felt and even thought.

The idea astounded me. It seemed there were dreams within dreams, dimensions within dimensions of dreams, arising from an endless inner source, protruding outward into the dream of the physical world. What did it all mean?

I paused in thought and looked curiously about the stone room I was building and, using the strength in my now powerful arms, I lifted myself over the wall into the open. I walked to the grove of trees where I stopped, leaning back against the small trunk of a juniper, shading myself under its branches. I opened the jar of beer that Marpa's wife had given me and drank slowly and deeply, aware of the presence of pleasure as the thick, cool liquid soothed my parched throat. At the same time, I was also aware of the striking pain throbbing in my knee. The contrast of pain and pleasure struck me. If mind was the source of dreams, the instrument that made us feel and react within the environment, the physical world, then life itself was merely a dream, a waking dream.

I recalled the dream-like feelings I had had while wandering naked on the mountainside. It was the feeling, the knowledge that I was dreaming or sleep-walking, and I recalled sensing that I was about to awaken.

Did that awakening ever come?

I gazed into the distance, seeing only the hillside at first and then what appeared to be small dark specks, which were the houses below in the valley. I wondered if I were merely witnessing a dream and, if so, was I dreaming that I was dreaming? And, if mind was indeed the dreamer that created life, then who was that other part of me that was aware of the mind's workings? Who was it that watched the dream? What was it?

Was the watcher that eternal part of myself that was said to outlive the body? I had heard my beloved Zesay speak of the consciousness in that manner. Often, following her visits with the good Lama Kataka, she would tell me the mysteries she had unraveled: Consciousness and its eternal evolution, how it unfolded and awakened a little bit more with each lifetime. The idea had fascinated me, although I had never understood it.

I smiled at the memory. I had rejected Zesay's offer to join her for study with the Lama Kataka. And now I was yielding my spirit before another guru in hopes of learning that which I had refused to learn. Perhaps if I had listened and learned from Lama Kataka, I would not now require Marpa's secrets. I would not have to build his house in exchange for a promise of his knowledge. I lifted the jug of the thick chang beer to my lips and drank again. I was about to reach for a piece of dried meat when I saw Marpa coming over the rise. I sat up suddenly.

"So this is how you build my house," Marpa called out, as if he had caught me loafing.

I stumbled to my feet, limping forward, favoring my badly bruised knee. "No, sir," I said quickly. "I injured my knee with a stone and I was resting it."

Marpa's eyes moved slowly from my eyes to my knees. He studied the discolored flesh around my knee. "Great sorcerer, I see that you are still using your powers," Marpa said, shaking his head from side to side. "Of course, it is better that you maim yourself than others. You do know about your powers?"

I lowered my eyes and then raised them again. "I am beginning to realize the power of thought and word," I said, hoping to find a way to tell the guru about my dream discoveries.

"Only beginning! You will, no doubt, kill yourself before you do," Marpa said, "or have you injured other things, as well." He hesitated, turning and looking about, as if expecting to see some injured creature on the ground. Seeing nothing, his gaze rested on the structure I was building. He walked over to it and strolled soberly around the outside and looked inside as he did.

I watched Marpa walk around the house, my heart racing in his silence. The guru's expression was somber.

When he had gone the distance around the house, Marpa approached me, shaking his head. "It will not do," he said firmly. "You have built me a monument of negative thought." He stopped, staring at me, as if waiting for me to explain myself.

I was too shocked to speak. The guru's eyes seemed to see through me, exposing me. I sensed that he knew about the injured crow and all of the other feelings I had had that caused me pain while I worked on the stone structure. I had been aware of my mind and the negative outflow of it but there had seemed no recourse. It was as if it had to empty itself out. But then, if Marpa knew of that side of me, he also knew of my dream discoveries. I was about to ask him when he interrupted me.

"You must tear it down," the guru instructed. "Tear it down and build another house. Do not use even one of these stones when you start again. They are tainted with your behavior, your words, and your thoughts. You must use only fresh stones. Is that understood?"

I suddenly felt desperate. "There must be some other way," I blurted out, limping forward. "If you would teach me, as promised, then the house would probably be more to your liking."

"In what way would it be more to my liking?" Marpa asked, eyeing me.

"The secret doctrines you possess would be flowing into me and from me, filling my work, if you taught me now," I said. I was pleading, using the only means I could think of to ensnare the help of the guru.

"You think you can bribe me?" Marpa growled in return.

"No, no, my guru. I do not think I can bribe you." I hesitated, trying to choose my words carefully. "I wish only to please you."

"Snail," Marpa snapped. "You approach me like a slow, sneaking, slippery slug. You do me no favor by building me a house. I do you a favor by allowing you to build me one. I don't need your work or any house you could build. I have a house."

"Indeed, you do," a woman's voice suddenly called out. It was Marpa's wife Nadar. She had come up from behind, carrying supplies for me and had not been seen. "You do have a house, and there is no need for you to torment this poor boy. Teach him what he asks and let him go in peace."

"Enough," Marpa growled, turning on his heels to face Nadar. "Your sympathy with this boy will result in his destruction. Leave your provisions of food and drink and go. Return home with the understanding that you have tried to interfere with my business."

"Teach the boy and let him be," Nadar pleaded. "Don't torture him."

Marpa glared angrily at his wife until she turned away. He watched her carry the provisions to the grove of trees and place them beneath, giving us a backward glance before she set off down the hill. Finally, he turned to me again. His expression had softened, although still stern. "If you wish my instruction," he said coolly, "you will have to earn it."

I hesitated, suddenly torn between belief and disbelief. The sympathy that Nadar had given me further weakened me. I saw myself as one who was unjustly tortured and persecuted, and I considered seeking the teaching of another guru, but did not wish to leave nor did I know where to go.

"Rebuild this house and I will teach you what you wish to know," Marpa said. "I will promise you that."

I lowered my eyes. I could no longer believe him.

"Milarepa," Marpa said gently, "I knew of your coming to this valley long before you arrived." He paused. I looked up. "I knew that I was to teach you when we first met at the feast outside your village. I knew it when I gave you short-cut directions into Tsang, when I guided Thither to find you in the forest. I could not tell you then because you were too busy living out your destiny, although it didn't have to be so. You didn't have to fulfill your mother's request, but you believed you did, and so you did. In so doing, your arrival here in Nar was delayed and with you came the baggage of a sorcerer's karma. It must be shed before you can share in what I wish to share with you. In building the house I request, you have been, and are still, rebuilding yourself. Do you understand me, Milarepa?"

Tears rushed into my eyes. For a moment, I had difficulty seeing and then they cleared again. "You promise, you will then teach me when I am finished?" I asked.

"Yes," Marpa said, "but you must tear this structure down and start over with a fresh set of stones and a clean mind guiding you."

I agreed.

After the guru left me alone, I carefully considered the task at hand. It had already taken me several weeks to build the house to this point, and it seemed fruitless to tear down the work that was already completed, merely to rebuild it stone for stone in exactly the same spot. If I left the back side of it as it was and merely tore down the front side and then continued building, Marpa could not possibly know about it. Once the building was completed, there would be no evidence whatsoever. My decision made, I set to work to finish the house.

Nearly a cycle of the moon passed before I finished Marpa's house. In that time, I rarely rested and only left the hill occasionally to acquire food and beverage from those in the valley below. During the last few days, I fully expected to see the guru suddenly behind or before me, appearing as he had always done at some propitious moment, but he did not come. When the house was finished, I took a slow walk around it, admiring the skill that I had gained, noticing the perfect balance with which the stones were set, and how I had engineered rounded corners rather than sharp angular ones. There was no doubt that the house, with its six rooms, was the finest around.

I turned around, looking from the hill at the spectacular view of the valley below, priding myself on making it possible for the guru Marpa to live in the highest spot in all the land. I had truly prepared a gift for the guru, one which I considered fair exchange for the teachings that the Lama had promised me. And so, with this thought in mind, I set off down the road to tell Marpa that his house was finished and to claim my reward.

Nadar met me at the door, her eyes downcast as if she was not pleased to see me.

"I have, at last, finished the guru's house," I said lightly, hoping to lift her spirits into a warmer greeting.

Nadar glanced up at me and then looked down again,

shaking her head. She did not step back from the doorway. "He will not see you," she said.

"But why?" I asked. "I have done as he asked. For nearly a cycle of the moon, I have labored to build his house and now he owes me the debt of his teaching."

Nadar did not look up again and did not answer me. She merely stood quietly, barricading the doorway with her presence.

"I insist," I said angrily. "I have spent much time building and rebuilding to suit the translator Marpa. Now, at last, when my task is finally completed, you tell me your husband will not see me. I won't stand for it," I shouted. "Tell Marpa to pay his debts!"

Just then there was a thunderous noise from inside the house and Marpa appeared, moving his wife from the doorway. His gigantic presence towered over me. He, too, was angry. "What is it you want?" Marpa growled at me.

I was too astonished to speak. The guru had met me as though I was a stranger, as though he did not even know me. "I have come to tell you that the house that you asked me to build for you is completed," I said finally.

Marpa did not speak but stood in the doorway glaring at me.

"May I take you to see it, my guru," I said, confused by the giant man's cool reception. "It is a house you can be proud of, two stories high with eight windows and six rooms. In addition, the kitchen has a special cooking place at the far wall where the smoke from Nadar's food preparations vents to the outside." I paused, seeing no change in the guru's expression, and then continued. "It is an exceptionally well-built house, with rounded corners instead of the usual square ones, and while building it, I did not incur a single moment of anger at myself or others, nor did I contemplate harm to any being, living or dead."

Marpa did not speak but suddenly turned around, his back to me.

I was crushed but angry and my heart pounded wildly at the insult. "You cannot turn your back on me," I suddenly shouted. "I have built a house to your specifications, with your promise that, in exchange, you will teach me all that you know." I paused, breathing loudly. "You owe me!" I yelled.

Marpa did not turn around but spoke in a quiet voice. "I have tried to give you purpose and to instill a sense of honesty in carrying out that purpose. I have tried to show you the joy of service and yet you have missed the point of it by your schemes. There is nothing I can teach you, as you have proven this yourself, so therefore, I ask you to go on your way. Find yourself another guru."

I was outraged and started to reach forward to strike Marpa on the back, when suddenly the guru turned to face me. My arm hung suspended, until finally, under the guru's unexpected compassionate gaze, I felt ashamed and lowered it. At the same time, unable to look at the guru, I lowered my eyes. There was a long silence in which I was conscious of every breath I took.

"You wish me to teach you, and yet you reject my instructions," Marpa said in a quiet voice. "What else am I to do but to send you to another guru, whose instruction you may be able to accept."

"But I did not reject your instruction, my guru." I said, raising my eyes.

"You think that because you have built me a fine house that I would not know that that part of the house that I asked you to tear down still stands," Marpa said, watching me. "Is that not so?"

Marpa knew, but how did he know? I wanted to lower my eyes again and to look away, but I was held by Marpa's all-seeing gaze, and I knew that the guru was looking into me as well as looking at me. I was too humbled to speak.

"You think I have been cruel to you," Marpa said, "but in truth, I have been nothing but kind to you. The disciplines I have set before you are gentle ones in comparison to the deeds you have committed. Had I coddled you with sympathy and gentle words you would either be dead or mad by now. Knowing this, I channeled your energies into constructive labor. The first house that you built was so crudely filled with your negativity that sensations from it contaminated the valley, and so I instructed you to tear it down. The second construction was only somewhat better, and so, before you had gotten too far, I asked that you level it and begin again. Instead, you insisted on continuing to build on that negative foundation. You believed that because you did not directly contemplate harm to any being, living or dead, that the nature of the structure changed. Did it ever occur to you that the house is now a product of your deceit?"

Marpa paused, gazing into me, and then said, "In constructing the house against my instructions, you plotted deception against me. Such deception, standing high on the hill over my home, in plain sight, has been a forward messenger that you think your guru to be a fool and not worthy of you at all." He paused again. "That is why I told you to seek another guru. There is nothing more I can teach you."

I clearly saw what Marpa was saying, as if the words were encircled in light, and I felt so greatly ashamed that I could not answer. My heart ached and, silently within myself, I cried out. It was a bad dream this dream of my life. Tears of shame poured down my face.

Marpa turned and disappeared through the dark doorway, leaving me alone.

I stood alone before the door of my guru. My heart was heavy, and I could not control the tears that streamed down my face. I had been a fool, playing Marpa for a fool, and although I had not seen it that way at the time I was building the house, I now knew that it was true. How could I be so stupid?

The doorway before me was dark. There was not a sound coming from Marpa's house. I wanted to call out to the guru, to ask his forgiveness, but the words would not come. The guru had rejected me, and I knew that nothing I could think to say would change it. Finally, after what seemed an eternity, I turned away.

I was shocked back into the nightmarish dreamworld I had experienced while I was alone in the mountains, only this time I was not in the mountains. I stood on the small hill above Marpa's home, gazing at the structure I had built for the guru. An occasional gust of wind brushed past me, pushing the thick rope of my tied-back hair forward until it touched my face. My chest heaved with the trauma I was feeling and, for a moment, I considered ending my life. To die would be of no positive consequence, however, and I knew it. To die with the weight of my grievous deeds would mean eternal doom. I had not improved my condition by building the guru's house, as I had believed. Now, aware of the deception I had practiced during those long days of construction, I realized I had compounded my errors instead of lessening them.

I walked over to the house I had built and touched the rounded corner of the outside kitchen wall with my hand. To leave the house standing would be to leave a monument to my deception. Leaning down, I picked up a discarded rock from the ground and struck it hard against the wall near the fire opening on the kitchen wall. The stone loosened the rock on the wall, and I struck it again, forcing it from the strategic position. Then I knocked out the one next to it and the ones next to that, gradually dismantling the house stone by stone, wall by wall.

It took me several days to totally level the house and several more to remove all the stones from the area. I had intended to leave when the job was finished, but then it occurred to me that if I rebuilt the house, I would in some way erase some of the wrong I had done. I did not expect the guru Marpa to accept or forgive me, or even to use the house after it was rebuilt. I merely saw the rebuilding of it as an opportunity to do something constructive for myself, to end the waking dream pleasantly, and so I began rebuilding.

CHAPTER THIRTEEN
NEW FREEDOMS

For the first time since I had left my mother's house, I enjoyed a life without expectation. It was my goal to carry out a task that had been given to me, and I did it, not for the pleasure of others, but for the sheer joy of doing it. I worked consistently, leaving the hill only for a few hours a week to beg food in the community below.

The people of the village were aware that I had fallen out of grace with Marpa but they didn't question me. Instead, meeting me, they would eye me curiously and then look up to the hill. The structure, which I had torn down, was rising again, and because I had not quit, the further along I got, the greater their willingness to give increased. When the second story was completed, many people gave me extra gifts of food, not merely barley grain and tsamba, but meat and vegetables. Often I was met with a smile and a jar of chang beer.

But the building did not stop at two stories. I had grown accustomed to the work and the solitude of the hill. I knew that someday I would have to leave, but first, I would build until I felt that the building was complete. So it turned out that for nearly a year I worked on the house. When finally I finished, the structure was a monument, towering above the valley. I had built Marpa's house nine stories high.

On the day that I finished, I fashioned a comfortable position beneath the bodhi tree and sat back to rest, sipping from a container of barley beer as I studied the end product of my work. As I sat looking up at the nine-story house, I was completely at peace. I marveled at my mental state, remembering what I was like when I had first come to the valley.

The greatest difference between then and now, it seemed, was that then my mind was filled with terrifying fantasies. I had been filled with inner turmoil and worry. My fears oppressed me to the very point of damnation. Now I was at peace with myself. Although I didn't know what tomorrow would bring, I sensed that I was no longer damned. The reason for this new freedom was that I was no longer filled with anticipation for anything. Marpa's year-long silence was an omen that nothing was expected of me, and so I expected nothing in return.

Although I had no idea of where I would go, I decided that it was time for me to leave. I took one last day to tidy up the job I had done. I collected tall grasses and tied them together, fashioning a broom. When the handle was good and sturdy, I carried it to the top floor of Marpa's stone house and began to sweep it clean of the stone chips and grit that had accumulated during the construction. I carefully swept each floor, turning to inspect it before descending to the next lower level. Finally, satisfied that the house was clean, I went outside to gather my remaining supply of food for the journey ahead. To my surprise, Marpa was waiting.

I bowed respectfully to the guru, hesitating to rise again.

"You have done well, Milarepa," Marpa said in a sincere tone of voice. He again looked at the house and then at me.

I was still too surprised by his appearance to speak. It had been nearly a year since I had seen him.

Marpa gazed thoughtfully at me, telling me that I appeared much older than when he had last seen me. In a quiet voice, he said that my once slight build was now sturdy and strong and that there was a marked difference in my expression, as well, explaining that the lines of my face had firmed in a gentle way and he could see the determination and perseverance of character reflected there. He also commented that my eyes were clear and that he understood my heartfelt motives were pure. "You are ready," he said, pausing and looking deeply into me. "You are now ready to take the next step. Come!" he called, placing an arm on my shoulder. "Nadar awaits us for the evening meal."

Marpa had spoken so naturally, so matter-of-factly, that I felt that we had been apart for a few hours instead of a year. At first, I hesitated, thinking that the guru would suddenly change his mind, but gazing into his kindly eyes and seeing the tears that were filling them, my heart answered with a swell of joy. I had waited a long time, and now, at last, the guru had accepted me as his disciple. I moved closer to Marpa, beneath his great arm, feeling its warmth on my shoulder, as we walked down the hill together to feast in Nadar's kitchen.

Marpa stepped back for me to enter through the doorway. The aroma of fresh meat and tsamba filled the long, narrow kitchen. The eating mat had been rolled out, and seated alongside either side of it were the translator's disciples, all men older than myself, except one. The one was my good friend Thither and our eyes met as I entered with Marpa. There was so much that I wanted to say to Thither but, knowing that it was not yet time, I held my tongue.

Nadar came over and put an arm around me, giving me a gentle squeeze. As she released me, I looked at Thither, who was seated, grinning up at me.

Marpa went to the head of the gathering and sat down, motioning me to take the empty seat near the end of the eating mat.

"This is a celebration," Marpa said, raising his jar of beer in front of him. The others raised their jars as well. "The great sorcerer is welcomed to this household. He is to attend our gatherings and to study with us." Marpa hesitated, a twinkle in his eye, "that is, if we are not too commonplace for the great sorcerer, builder of nine-story monuments."

The others laughed good-naturedly, including Thither, who quickly looked at me. I knew that the laughter was for the spectacular accomplishment I had made and not intended as an insult.

"Cheers to the great sorcerer," Marpa called out.

"Cheers to the great sorcerer," the others repeated. Nadar,

too, raised a jar of beer and took a long, deep drink and then hurried to finish serving the food. When everyone was eating, she sat down next to me and joined the feast.

Mostly, the conversation was about the structure I had built. One man wanted to know what possessed me to continue construction after Marpa had dismissed me.

The question surprised me. I had taken it for granted that everyone who watched me constructing the guru's house knew why I did it. I glanced at Marpa, who paused in eating, waiting for me to speak.

"I had no place to go," I answered simply, lowering my eyes, embarrassed by the focus of everyone's attention.

"Is that it?" the man asked. "You stayed because you had no place to go."

I nodded, not knowing what else to say. After a year of solitude, I was unaccustomed to conversation. I glanced at Thither, who shrugged his shoulders, as if to say it didn't matter.

"But surely there is more to the reason than that?" the man prodded.

I nodded, uneasily. "Yes," I said, "there was." I stopped there, not wishing to expose my innermost feelings.

Marpa continued eating.

"Ah, but I suppose you knew that to construct such a structure would return you to the good graces of our teacher," the man said again.

Marpa appeared not to hear and continued eating.

I stared at the man. He had a thin, pinched-looking face and tiny slits for eyes. "You think what you like," I said, "however, what you say is not the truth. I rebuilt the house in an effort to rebuild myself, and in rebuilding myself, I held no expectations from the great translator Marpa."

The gathering fell silent again. Nadar touched me lightly on the knee, as if to encourage me.

"And did you use your sorcerer's powers?" the one next to the first man asked. He had a beard and bushy eyebrows that exaggerated the motions of his face as he spoke.

I hesitated, unsure of how to answer. All eyes were on me, except Marpa's. The guru continued to eat without looking up.

"Well," the man prodded.

"I am not sure how to answer," I said.

"And why is that?" the man asked.

"Because I am myself," I answered. "And if being myself means that I am the great sorcerer you call me, then I suppose I did use the sorcerer's powers. How can I separate myself from what I am?"

Everyone's attention was fully on me. I felt the warm flush of blood rushing to my face, and I lowered my eyes.

"Enough," Marpa called out, interrupting the uncomfortable silence. He put his bowl on the mat and glared at the man who had questioned me. The man lowered his eyes, as did the man next to him. "The great sorcerer is here because I invited him. His motives are not in question, and he is not to be challenged without the challenger first challenging me."

The eating stopped. Everyone lowered his eyes. There was a long silence in which no one moved. "Has no one anything pleasant to say at this celebration?" Marpa asked.

"I have looked forward to our reunion," Thither quickly said, looking at me. "Feasting again with Milarepa pleases me greatly."

I smiled gratefully at my friend.

When the eating was finished, Marpa rose suddenly and dismissed the others, telling me to find a suitable sleeping place, but to report to him before retiring.

Thither was quick to approach me after Marpa left, offering to share his sleeping quarters with me. He embraced me warmly and then held me at arm's length to look at me.

We did not speak for a long while, gazing at each other, as if looking into the experiences of the other.

Nadar stopped in her kitchen duties and watched us.

"I only recently returned from a journey north of here," Thither said finally. "I was gone for nearly the full year. Marpa sent me among some primitive people to study their way of life. I, too, learned something of black magic and how it works."

I didn't say anything but waited for him to continue, aware that he appeared older and more confident than I had remembered him.

"I came to realize that, because I once had a strong desire to understand magic, it had to come to pass." He paused, then continued, "Marpa calls it etching one's desires in the ethers.

Wherever I went, I was drawn to discoveries of how the practice of magic works." Thither placed an arm about my shoulders. "But the telling of my experiences can wait," he said.

"I would like to hear," I said curiously, sensing that Thither's discoveries could shed further light on my own. "Perhaps soon we will have time."

"We will, surely," Thither said.

"I am grateful for your friendship," I said, then I turned to Nadar and bowed. "I am glad for your friendship, as well, reverend mother," I added.

Nadar reached over and lightly touched my arm, then turned away.

"Do not forget that Marpa has asked that you see him," Thither said. "I have the feeling that he is waiting for you now."

Nadar turned quickly and put her face close to mine. "Yes," she said, "he is waiting in his private chamber. No doubt he will put some impossible task to you, so be prepared."

"What sort of task?" I asked, surprised. I had not considered that Marpa would test me further.

"Don't worry about it," Thither said. "Just go to him and do as he says."

I started to ask where I was to meet Marpa when Nadar pointed to a stairway at the far end of the hall that led to a room below the house. I had been there once before, a year ago. It was before Marpa had set me to the task of building a house for him. Hesitantly, I started down the hall, paused at the stairway, and then slowly descended. When I came to the guru's study, I hesitated again, looking through the open doorway, seeing Marpa seated as though he was a great lord, in silk robes atop a stack of embroidered cushions.

"Come in," Marpa said, seeing me.

I entered and stood before the guru.

"Sit down," Marpa said warmly, motioning to a plump cushion in front of him.

I sat down and hesitantly looked into the great guru's eyes. I remembered the time when I had first met the guru. I had believed him to be a farmer, plowing his field. Again, I felt the sheer ecstasy and lightness of body while gazing into the guru's eyes. It was as though a flow of pure love reached out from him and enclosed me.

"I have promised you all the knowledge I possess," Marpa said softly, "and so you shall have it." He motioned to the walls above and about his head where rolls of scrolls were stored. There were hundreds of them. "You shall study them all," he said, "and what you do not understand from them will become clear in your meditations." He paused, watching me. I felt deliriously happy. My innermost wish was being fulfilled. After a moment, he said, "But first, great sorcerer, you must give me a gift." Marpa paused, extending a hand, as though waiting for it to be filled with some gift I had brought him.

I had nothing and was too astounded to speak, remembering that Nadar had cautioned me to expect a shocking request from the guru. Finally, I answered. "But, my guru, all that I am and all that I have, you already see. I have no gifts, no possessions."

Marpa glanced down at his empty hand and withdrew it. "Then I cannot allow you to study with me," he said sadly.

I did not believe that I had heard him correctly and sat staring at him.

"I am sorry," Marpa said sadly. He lowered his eyes as if he were genuinely sorry but forced to reject me.

I was shocked. "But surely, that is not true," I said, sitting more erect and remembering the gaze of love the master had given me. "You came to the hill where I built your house and brought me home with you. If I was not welcome, why did you fetch me?"

"Because you are welcome," Marpa said sadly.

"But I don't understand."

"You must give me a gift before I can allow you to study," Marpa said again.

"But I have nothing," I cried.

"But surely for a man of power, a great sorcerer, you can conjure up something," Marpa said encouragingly.

I was greatly confused. Marpa had long ago said that he wanted nothing from me, that his favor couldn't be bought. He had cautioned me against ever using my sorcerer's powers, and now he was suggesting that I use them. It made no sense whatsoever.

"It is the way," Marpa said without explanation.

I stared at the guru, unsure if he were joking, but he remained serious. "What sort of gift do you require?" I asked.

"A personal possession of great value," Marpa answered. "It need not be large in size, only in importance."

I continued to stare at the guru. I had the feeling that at any moment he would burst out with a roar of laughter, but his expression remained sober.

"Do you understand me?" Marpa asked, his eyes full upon me.

I shook my head. "No," I said, "No, I do not understand."

"You do not understand my instructions?" Marpa asked.

"I do not understand why you ask for what I do not have," I said.

Marpa was silent a moment. His eyes were filled with pity. "It is a paradox and a riddle," he said. "Understanding cannot come without the gift and the gift cannot come without understanding." He rose from his seat and stood over me. "Leave me now. Come back when you have an offering. Then, and only then, can I offer you initiation into the secret teachings."

"Why do you bring me here only to reject me?" I asked, rising to my feet before him.

"I do not reject you," Marpa said sadly.

I stared at the guru, unsure if I were missing something in the context of things, uncertain as if I were caught in another fiendish dream. There could be no reality to what I was experiencing, and yet, there seemed to be nothing to awaken me from my living nightmare. After a long moment, I lowered my eyes, turned around, and left the room, walking slowly back down the long hallway to the kitchen area where Nadar and Thither waited.

Nadar clasped her hands to her breast and let out a short gasp as I re-entered the room. Thither reflected my stricken face and slumped shoulders.

"What has my husband done to you?" Nadar cried, wrapping her warm, chubby arms about me. She pulled my head next to her breast and held me there for a moment before releasing me. She looked into my eyes and, seeing the confusion there, turned to Thither. "Ask him," she said.

"What is the guru's request?" Thither asked.

I shook my head, as if to clear my thoughts.

"What is it?" Thither prodded.

"He requires a gift, a personal possession," I answered. "I have nothing." I paused, gazing into my friend's clear, bold eyes. "All that I had, I gave to the Lama Yungtun-Trogyal in exchange for his knowledge. Now, I have nothing, and yet Marpa says I must give him an offering before he is able to give me initiation."

Thither pursed his lips thoughtfully.

"Come here," Nadar called in a soft voice, motioning to me to follow her. She led me to the far end of the kitchen where she loosened a brick and removed it from the wall. Then she put her hand into the hole and drew out a large oval-shaped turquoise. It was obviously a very valuable piece. She quickly replaced the brick into the wall and handed me the turquoise. "Take it," she said. "Give it to Marpa as an offering for his secrets."

"But I cannot," I answered quickly. "I cannot give that which is not mine."

"I give it to you," Nadar said. "I give you the turquoise, and now that it is yours, you may give it to my husband."

"But he will know," I said.

Nadar shook her head. "He will not know," she said, without explaining. "He does not know I have it."

I turned to Thither, who seemed to be disturbed. "What do you advise?" I asked him.

Thither shrugged his shoulders and said he did not feel it wise to try and trick Marpa, but then reasoned that if Nadar had given me the gem, then it was not really a trick. Still, Thither appeared uneasy.

"There is no recourse," Nadar said to me. "You must take it. Go to Marpa now while he is still in his work chamber, and tell him that you found you did have a gift for him after all."

"But he will ask me where I got it," I said.

"It does not matter," Nadar said confidently. "The turquoise was mine alone, not his, and as such, it was mine to give to you and now is rightfully yours to give to him. He cannot refuse you."

I was uneasy and turned to Thither again, but Thither only shrugged his shoulders once more. His eyes widened at the idea.

"Go," Nadar said, urging me, turning me around and pointing me in the direction of Marpa's work room. Then she gave me a little push.

I started down the hall, down the steps, stopping before the entrance of Marpa's work chamber. The guru was seated with a scroll sprawled out before him. He looked up at me.

"What is it?" Marpa asked.

My whole body knotted with tension as I held out my hand containing the turquoise and stepped forward. I began to tremble.

Marpa stared at my outstretched hand and the turquoise. "Where did you get that?" he asked, a look of surprise on his face.

"Nadar gave it to me," I said weakly. "I now give the gift she gave me to you for initiation."

Marpa released the scroll he had been holding, allowing it to roll shut in his hand, put it down and then rose to his feet. "Nadar!" he roared. "Come here!"

As if shot from a bow, Nadar came running into the room. "Yes, my husband," she answered.

"Where did you get the turquoise that Milarepa holds in his hand?" Marpa demanded.

Nadar stood boldly before the giant man, her hands on her hips. "It was my personal property," she said, looking her husband in the eye. "It was given to me by my mother before our marriage to ensure my welfare in case our union did not last."

Marpa stared at Nadar with cold eyes.

"You are not considered an easy man to be with," Nadar said again, "not then any more than now."

"By law, your possessions are mine," Marpa said angrily. "You had no right to withhold the turquoise from me."

"Indeed, I did," Nadar said boldly. "It was mine, not yours, and I gave it to Milarepa. It is now your duty to accept it as his gift for initiation."

I lowered my eyes, wishing that I had never allowed Nadar to convince me to be a part of her scheme. The whole thing was turning out much worse than I had thought it would, much, much worse, in fact.

"Will you never learn to stop meddling," Marpa said to his wife. He put the turquoise into the pocket of his robe and sat down again. "Now both of you, get out of my sight."

I was filled with regret. I should have known that I would become involved in a family squabble. I started for the doorway.

"Wait," Nadar called after me. "The turquoise was mine to give you. It is only right that, if you gave it to Marpa, he owes you initiation."

"Quiet, woman!" Marpa roared, jumping to his feet. "The turquoise is rightfully mine, and therefore, cannot be a gift from the sorcerer."

I ran from the room and hurried back into the kitchen area again intending to rush outside, but Thither caught me by the arm and led me through another doorway into a sleeping room. No one else was there.

"The others have gone into Nar and will not return until tomorrow," he said, turning to me. "You can rest easy for the night."

I could not sleep, and after a while of lying perfectly still in the darkness, I arose and moved noiselessly past Thither, not wishing to disturb him, and stepped outside.

The cool night air drew my attention to the hill where I had built Marpa's nine-story house, recalling the many nights I had slept in the open there. I was accustomed to sleeping in the outdoors, and even though the weather had not always been agreeable, I preferred it to stuffy enclosures. Sleeping indoors reminded me too much of the Lama Yungtun-Trogyal's monastery and the stale, musty air that was trapped within it.

Remembering it all seemed so unreal. The one person who stuck out most in my mind was Narquin, and yet there was nothing real in my memories about him. Narquin had always seemed to be some mysterious by-product of the great Lama. I remembered how Narquin would seemingly appear and disappear, how sometimes while I looked at him, he would seem to change into the form of the Lama, and the thing about him that I remembered most was the pink-red glow that preceded his appearances and disappearances. It struck me strange that a high disciple of the dark force was preceded by such intense light.

I drew in a deep breath and slowly exhaled, feeling the rush of cool air clearing my thoughts. I began to walk, first without direction, and then to the very spot where I had lived during the past year. It seemed natural for me to ascend the hill to the nine-story monument I had erected. I walked slowly and deliberately and, for a time, my mind was still. I felt as though I was without body, as though I had died and was living in another dimension.

Finally, rising to the top of the hill, I paused and looked into the valley below. The valley houses were situated in little clusters, except Marpa's house. His stood alone at the base of the hill, a white prayer flag engraved with figures of enlightened men waving to me in a gentle breeze, nudging me to remember and to think of past deeds.

I thought of the turquoise Nadar had given me to give Marpa, and I also thought of the one my own mother had given me as a gift to the black magician. They were about the same size. Nadar's turquoise was a little deeper in color. I recalled, too, that Thither had been the bearer of my mother's turquoise, that he had been directed to find me in the forest by the cart driver, who was Marpa. Remembering, I considered the odd chain of events, how linked together they were, one connecting the other, and how Marpa, Thither, and I were linked together. Our union was timeless and yet timely, as though our lives were destined to overlap and, even though the guru had again turned me away from him, it didn't seem that I had ever really been separated from him since our first meeting.

The strange feeling of being without a body, of having died and moved into another dimension returned to me. Had I died after all? Was Narquin's prophecy of the experience of a living doom, an eternal damnation, fulfilling itself? Was Marpa's request for a gift that I didn't have a part of that prophecy of doom? I recalled the frequent dream-like feelings I had had since using the black magician's power on the village of Nyang, how the fiendish episodes enfolded me, and as I remembered, I unconsciously watched the prayer flag over Marpa's house, the movement of it dancing about in the wind.

To be rejected by Marpa now should not be so difficult. Until the guru had come to the hill a few hours ago, I had planned to leave Nar. Before Marpa's appearance, I had come to a point of indifference toward the guru's earlier rejection and had found comfort in not caring anymore. Now, the inner turmoil filled me all over again.

I dismissed the anger that tried to rush into me. I did not want to be angry. If the guru rejected me again, what did it matter?

Asking the question of myself started a mental argument. It did not matter and yet it did. There was a part of me that seemed already joined to him. How could the bond truly be severed? Besides, the guru had said that he was not rejecting me. He had said merely that the offering of a gift was the way to initiation. Of course, I had known this, it was why I had given everything to the black magician in exchange for his power. Only now, I had nothing left to give. Why was the gift so important? It seemed to me that a guru should give initiation freely to those who earnestly seek it, without payment of any kind.

Suddenly resentful, the anger rose in me again and I struggled within myself to silence it. I could not bear the consequences of exercising a burst of anger. I did not wish to injure anyone or anything, including myself. I thought of the incident at Marpa's well.

In the struggle to maintain inner peace, I realized that a part of the anger I felt was due to feeling impoverished. I had been born with wealth and then had it taken from me. I felt sorry for myself, for the injustices that had been dealt me. It wasn't that I wanted many possessions, but I wished to have something to give. I argued within myself, concluding that, although I did not have material possessions to give, I did have the physical power to work. I had employed both that power and my imagination to build the house for Marpa. Was not the house a gift to Marpa?

The answer came suddenly. The house I had built for Marpa was not truly for the guru. I had built the house for myself, as a penance for my misdeeds and failures and, moreover, I used the construction of it as a tool to balance the forces within myself. It was because I had balanced these forces, I supposed, that Marpa had come to me.

The prayer flag rose and fell in swift, graceful motions and, watching it, I realized that it was torn. The edges were jagged and it was ripped in the center. As I stood watching it rise and fall in the wind, I became fascinated, piecing it together in my imagination, likening it to the length of white wool that had been given to me as a blanket by Nadar and Thither during my illness on the hill nearly a year ago, and it occurred to me that I could turn my wool blanket into a suitable flag.

The gift to Marpa for initiation!

The idea soared in me. I tried to calm myself, arguing to myself that the cloth had come from Nadar and Thither, that the guru might reject it as a gift as he had done the turquoise. Then, suddenly, I didn't care. I would take my wool blanket and turn it into a prayer flag as a gift to Marpa. If he rejected it as an initiation gift, I would give it to him anyway, then I would leave as I had previously planned.

The next morning, I spread the wool blanket in front of me on the ground and studied the surface of it. It was a rough piece of cloth, but it would do and, actually, the coarseness of it would make it a sturdy companion for the wind. The question now was what impression to set upon it.

I rose and went to the side of the hill, looking down to where I had seen Marpa's flag the night before, but it hung limp and lifeless in the still air. I tried to recall any figures or special markings on the flag but the light had been poor and, except for remembering that I had seen them, I couldn't remember what the designs had been.

I turned and walked slowly back to the wool blanket. The only prayer designs that I had ever truly paid attention to were in the prayer room at the monastery of the black magician. I thought about what I had seen there, how the walls above each drum depicted a story of the prayer itself.

Standing above the fleece, I thought of Thither and how when first we met, he had told me of a rock in Nar that had the image of the Buddha painted upon it. I had never seen it but had imagined it from Thither's description. The Buddha supposedly sat in lotus position and extending from him were warm rays of light.

I remembered, too, that Zesay had had a wallhanging near the entrance to her house. I had seen it many times. The hanging had been a gift from the Lama Kataka. I tried to recall the details of that wall hanging but very little came to mind, an image symbolic of a state of consciousness, yet different from the one Thither had described. The image had seemed rather bland and uninteresting, a figure of a faceless person. On occasion, Zesay had tried to draw my attention to a small odd-shaped object over the Buddha's head, which she had called a Dorje. She had said that the Dorje symbolized the protector of truth, telling me that, if I spoke and acted in the name of truth, with love and sincerity, from the heart, the outcome of my deeds were protected, that even if I mistakenly acted wrongly, the Dorje would neutralize the effects. Although at the time I regarded her explanation as primitive superstition and had rejected it, I now regarded the object, not as an object of power, but as a symbol of a principle, which comforted me.

Looking out across the hill, scanning the familiar terrain, my gaze rested on a clump of bushes that had tiny purple flowers on them. I recalled watching Zesay as she collected such flowers to use as a dye for painting designs on cloth. Excited and filled with a sense of purpose, I hurried over to them.

The first bush that I came upon was the indigo plant, and I then found the teisa plant with its tiny red flowers. There was also goldenrod growing wild on the hill. I spent some hours gathering the flowers and stems of these plants until, finally confident that I had gathered enough, I carried them to the tree under which I had spread out my blanket. First, I placed the indigo and teisa buds on a flat rock to dry. Later, when the sun had dried them crisp, I used a smaller rock to grind them into a fine powder. When I had finished, I rose to my feet again and carefully chose some fine blades of tall grass and picked them down near the roots. I put them down at my feet and then reached to the back of my head and parted my hair. From high on my scalp, I pulled out a small clump of hair and then evened the ends of it with my fingers and slowly wound the fine grasses firmly about them until only a small portion remained visible at the very tip. I brushed the instrument against my forefinger to test it. It was soft and pliable. Finally, carefully, I poured a few drops of water into two tiny crevices in the rock, next to the powders, and dipped my brush first into the liquid and then into the powder, mixing each dye into a thin ink. When I had finished, I turned my attention to the blanket.

I drew the form of the seated person, as I had seen it on Zesay's wall, a faceless image depicting a consciousness rather than a personality. The hands of the person were outstretched and about it were rays of light. Above the figure, directly overhead, was the Dorje, a small urn-like vessel suspended in space over the head of the form.

I moved back from my work, studying the form I had painted, my eyes forever drawn to the faceless face and to the Dorje overhead. There was a sadness to the image; at least when I paused over it, I felt sadness, as though the image was reaching out to me, offering me something I did not recognize. The feeling was one of longing for something, although that something had no name. The feeling was one that made me wish that my life would suddenly end, that I could close my eyes and return home to someplace I did not even remember. I wished, too, that the meaning of the image on the blanket would somehow enter my heart and fill me, that my gift to Marpa would be a true gift, given in recognition of this knowledge.

I turned away and rose to my feet. A tear formed in the corner of my eye and I quickly wiped it away. I wanted to finish the prayer flag, and yet, the finishing of it was no longer for Marpa, but for myself. There had been a bittersweet quality to the task, like biting into a bittersweet candy. It tasted good, but there was also a quality of pain in the sweetness of its taste.

Gazing down at the painted blanket, I felt a great pull within myself. Uncertain, I remained standing above it, wondering at the feeling. Why did the image of the faceless one move me so? A part of me wanted not to finish the prayer flag. I thought instead of rolling it up, digging a deep hole and burying it in a place where it would not be likely to be found. It was an absurd thought, of course, but nevertheless, an impulse of which I was strongly aware. Why would I wish to bury Marpa's prayer flag? Why did I not wish to destroy it instead?

I knelt down over the image I had painted, continuing to stare at it. Again, tears came into my eyes. While part of me wanted to bury the image deep into the ground, another part wished to exalt it. It seemed only fitting that it hang attached to a pole, flying in the breeze. I loved it, not the cloth or the painting on it, but what the painting symbolized.

What did it symbolize?

I looked into the blank space where the face should have been, noticing that the rough nap of the fleece made it appear that there was some definition there. I smoothed it with my hands but the definition was still there. I could see the subtle outline of a mouth, lips slightly curved upward in the hint of a smile. Just above it, a nose and then three eyes—two beneath the eyebrows and the third directly above and between the other two. I tilted my head to one side to see if the angle eliminated the definition, but it was the same. The expression of the faceless face seemed very nearly alive.

It was absurd. I rose to my feet again and went over to the rough stone house I had built, gazing up at it from below. Life had little meaning to me anymore. It used to be that Zesay filled my life with meaning, but her love had been torn from me. Indeed, I had been stripped of everything that had once had meaning to me. My sister Peta had been swallowed into the bowels of Katmandu and my mother was dead. My own life had been of no use. My accomplishments had been destructive rather than constructive. I was a mere shadow of a man celebrating a life that was lifeless.

Standing there, I remembered a time when, as a boy, Zesay found me outside my mother's home feeling sorry for myself about the unfair circumstances in my family's life. She told me not to think on it, that the thinking confused and angered my feelings and that the hardship I was feeling would be exaggerated by negative thought. I was amazed at Zesay's comments and yet I instinctively knew them to be true. I knew them to be true now, as well, and yet a part of me could not help but feel sorrow at the state of my life. I wished that I had something more to give. Then an idea struck me. I hurried back to the blanket spread out beneath the tree and knelt before it. Lifting the brush, I dipped it into the purple dye. Then, at the feet of the faceless one, I designed a bowl, overflowing with sweetmeats, fruit, and flowers. When I had finished, I leaned back on my heels to see what I had done.

The picture took on a new meaning. Now, with the addition of flowers and food, it was plain to see that a gift had been laid out before the great consciousness. I was pleased with what I had done.

When the ink dried, I carefully folded the blanket, draped it over my arm, and went down the hillside with it to find Marpa.

Marpa was in the yard in front of his house with Thither and the other disciples. They were standing near the well conversing when Marpa, as if sensing my presence, suddenly turned and extended an arm to welcome me.

I was surprised but went to the guru, standing next to him under the length of his great arm.

"It is good you have returned," Marpa said affectionately. I slowly turned my head and gazed up at the guru who stood nearly a foot taller than me. "I returned to the hill and noticed that the prayer flag above your house was torn by the wind," I said. "I made a new one for your house." I hesitated, then handed him the neatly folded blanket. My heart pounded with excitement as the guru took it from me. Marpa handed one end to Thither and another to a man I did not know and asked them to hold it up for him to see.

For a long while Marpa stood silently, examining the prayer flag. When finally he turned to me, he had tears in his eyes. "I accept your gift, my son," Marpa said clearly. "Go into the house and tell Nadar that you are to bathe in preparation, that she is to give you a clean robe for initiation." I hesitated, struck by joy, and gazed into the guru's glowing face. After a moment, Marpa nodded to me and smiled, indicating that I should go. I quickly turned and went toward the house.

Nadar waited in the doorway, smiling triumphantly at me. She hugged me, then quickly led me inside.

"Knowledge tears away the supernatural mysteries, which have formed hiding places for man's consciousness. Knowledge is the illuminator and in its light there is no shadow, no opposites, no good, no bad."

CHAPTER FOURTEEN
INITIATION

I approached Marpa's private chamber in a new cotton robe. My freshly scrubbed skin tingled beneath it, and in the excitement of the moment, my entire life flashed before me like drawings on a wall, crowding my mind with images of places I had been and things I had done that had led me to this moment. Most of all, I thought of Zesay, not so much as a woman attracting me but as a force that had moved me to this point in my spiritual development. She was, in some way, a symbol of the initiation I was about to receive.

Marpa rose to his feet and welcomed me inside. He, too, was dressed in a clean cotton robe and his hair was neatly tied back in a knot behind his head. He motioned that I sit before him. He smiled at me and then his expression became serious. "You have asked for knowledge," he said, "and so I must forewarn you that the gifts of knowledge are without heaven and hell. Knowledge tears away the supernatural mysteries, which have formed hiding places for man's consciousness. Knowledge is the illuminator, and in its light there is no shadow, no opposites, no good, no bad." He paused, looking deeply into me.

I flushed, feeling as though the guru was looking inside me, seeing me exactly as I was, without camouflage of any kind, and I realized that, in seeking and being granted initiation, I had given the guru permission to enter into my innermost being.

"Through proper training, you will learn to contemplate and to meditate on your contemplations," Marpa said. "You will pass through many stages of contemplation, and each one you pass through will bring greater knowledge and awareness of your mental distractions. You will come to recognize the reasons for your mental flow. The foundations of your feelings will be laid bare before you. You will see how attitudes, aberrations, and facsimiles interact and how they focus the attention to create one's physical circumstances. Through constant practice, you will realize that the true, balanced state of the individual is achieved through contemplation or through distraction from it, and that contemplation and distraction are merely other forms of opposites."

Marpa paused again, this time flattening his hands over his large lap. He looked at his hands, flexed them, and then looked back at me. "You will know that you have accomplished the Buddha state when all hope for spiritual glories are dissipated and when the fear of not achieving them is also gone, when, in actuality, no hope or fear for anything exists within you." Marpa paused again but this time he did not move. He looked steadily into my eyes without speaking.

Gazing into the guru's eyes, I was oddly aware that objects about us in the room had seemingly receded, that nothing was truly visible to me but Marpa, and that I sat without thought, like a sponge, soaking up the very essence of the moment. The silence was so intense that in it I seemed to hear a thin, high-pitched, piercing sound coming to me from a great distance. The sound was faint, but as I listened, it seemed to grow louder.

"Close your eyes," Marpa said softly.

I felt my eyelids flutter, as if a part of me resisted, but then they closed. To my amazement, beneath closed eyelids, Marpa's face was still in front of me. It was as though I had not closed my eyes at all. The thin, high-pitched sound of silence grew louder, then softened and assumed a graceful swing to it, like the music played on a foreign stringed instrument, more refined than the lute, which Zesay had often played for me. My attention was caught by it. It was haunting and beautiful, unlike any other music I had ever heard, and the longer I listened, the more it flowed through me. I had the sensation that I was being consumed by the music. I also had the knowledge that Marpa was connected to it, that while the music came from elsewhere, Marpa and I were connected to it, and connected to each other by it. Then, as though in a dream, I heard Marpa ask me if I still wished initiation.

"Yes!" I heard myself answer aloud. There was a sudden break in the silence, in the musical voice of it, and I opened my eyes.

Marpa smiled at me and reached forward and kissed me on both cheeks, then he rose to his feet and went to the shelves against the wall. He withdrew two rolled parchments and handed them to me. "Study these," he said, "and then contemplate their meaning. When you believe you understand them, come and share your realizations with me."

I took the scrolls and returned to the hillside where I had built Marpa's house, remaining outside under the bodhi tree. I put one scroll gently on the ground at my side and the other on my lap where I carefully unrolled it. I read:

> Should one cling to the reality of visions,
> he would become confused in his contemplation.
> One must know that all obstacles
> are manifestations of mind;
> that, in truth, they reveal the void,
> which is of the same illusionary nature.

I read the passage over again and then permitted the parchment to roll closed in my hands. My mind was suddenly without thought, as though it had been struck a strong blow and, for a moment, was stunned into not thinking. I picked up the second scroll, unrolled it and read:

> In the realm of illumination,
> where subject and object are one,
> there is no cause and no effect.
> Here in this unity, all is void.
> It is timeless,
> when the actor and acting disappear,
> and all existence becomes correct.

I closed the second parchment and put it aside, as well, looking out over the hillside to the valley below. I sat there for a long while before I became aware of Thither's presence. I looked up suddenly to see him standing nearby, a sack in his hand.

"I did not wish to interrupt your concentration," Thither said pleasantly, coming toward me. "Nadar sends you food and extends an invitation to stay at Marpa's house. As for myself, I will be glad to share my room with you. The others have gone to Digur to study at the monastery there." He put the sack next to me beneath the tree and paused, kneeling next to it. He looked first at me and then at the towering nine-story house I had built for Marpa.

I wanted to speak, to share a moment of friendship with Thither but, still engrossed in the parchments Marpa had given me to study, I could think of nothing to say.

Thither looked from the house to me and said, "I can understand your desire for solitude and I respect it. Come and stay with me at Marpa's house when you wish to do so." He rose to his feet.

I thanked him for the food and nodded gratefully. I was relieved when Thither quickly turned and left me sitting alone. I opened the second scroll again.

> In the realm of illumination, where subject and
> object are one, there is no cause and no effect .....

I paused, thinking of what Marpa had said during my initiation; that knowledge was without shadows; that good and bad were illusionary, and I thought of the deeds I had done in my life, how I had brought destruction to my village; and I wondered how it could be true. I continued to read:

> Here in this unity, all is void.
> It is timeless,
> when the actor and acting disappear,
> and all existence becomes correct.

Was it possible that I could ever reach this state; that I could move beyond the curse of the black arts brought about by the damage I had done to the villagers of Nyang? It didn't seem possible, and yet, I was hopeful.

My thoughts reeled in conflict and confusion. Surely there was an error in the scroll. Perhaps someone had copied it wrong. Could it be that Marpa meant to trick me? Was realizing the error in the scroll a part of my initiation?

I opened the first scroll a second time.

Should one cling to the reality of visions,
he would become confused in his contemplation.

I paused, struck by the nature of the statement. It was almost as if my conflicting thoughts had been anticipated. Was I not now contemplating the reality of my memories? Were they the visions that were confusing me?

As I continued the argument within myself, I grew sleepy, and leaning my head against the trunk of the tree, I closed my eyes.

A soft, trickle of a breeze brushed my cheek, lifting the hair on my forehead and then dropping it again. It felt as if someone's hand had moved across my brow in a soothing motion, and I thought of Zesay, remembering how I had thought of her moments before my initiation, how I had considered that she had a power within her that had attracted me into initiation. The force she carried was womanly, distinctly female, and yet its persuasive quality was more than a physical stimulus. Her being represented a force in my life, one that matched my own force, but with an opposite strength— she the female, I the male; she the yielding strength, while I the opposite of her by nature, and although I didn't understand the true meaning of that difference, I sensed that my power was a strength that dominated and possessed. I paused, trying to think more deeply on the subject. Although Zesay was being defined as the passive or yielding force, I knew that her strength was no less than my own. Perhaps I had thought of her before initiation in order to recognize her female force, to be nurtured by her nature, suggesting to myself that I must yield to the possessing force of my guru in order to receive initiation.

Shadows on the hillside began to deepen and, for awhile, I sat not thinking but watching the play of the light with the darkness, how the wind made the shadows of the scraggly brush dance to and fro in the receding light. I felt a sudden urge for Zesay, to catch a glimpse of her joy and understanding as I told her what I had discovered. The pain of separation made me call out to her, to tell her that our love was a spiritual union of her force with my force, a force that linked together not only me with her, but her with Marpa, as well.

I closed my eyes, expecting to see a soft image of Zesay's face, but instead, I was looking into Marpa's eyes, forgetting her, aware only of the mysterious silence that enveloped Marpa's face in front of my own. The silence was haunting, flowing with unearthly music. Gazing into the guru's eyes, I was drawn into the alluring music of the silence, fascinated by it, enraptured by it, filled with joy and bliss and, for an instant, I understood all that had been written on the parchment—the unity of the light and the void of mind, an instant when the actor and acting disappeared, and all existence became correct. There could be nothing but correct existence in that state where no opposition could exist.

My inward conclusion brought sudden argument to mind. How could I forgive myself for the deeds I had done against the people of Nyang? My peace of mind faded as I tried to reason it out, and I opened my eyes. The image of Marpa and the music of silence disappeared. I was suddenly greatly disturbed.

Toward the middle of the next day, Thither came again. This time I was lying face down, my chin resting in my hands, lost in thought while seemingly looking out over the valley. I suddenly heard a snap and looked up to see Thither, standing there holding a broken branch in his hands. As though in a dream, I gazed up at him.

Thither dropped the broken branch to the ground. "I did not want to startle you, my friend," he said smiling. "I bring you greetings from our guru Marpa. He asks that you return to his house to meet with him in his private chambers."

I calmly studied Thither and then, as if I had suddenly heard what he had said, I reached for the parchments Marpa had given me and quickly rose to my feet.

Thither hesitated, as though wanting to speak, but said nothing. Instead, he motioned that I follow him down the hill.

Marpa's study chamber was empty and yet, as I entered to wait for the guru, I had the strangest feeling that I was not alone. I looked about the small room, expecting to see someone, but no one was there. Finally, I sat down, taking the seat I had used during my initiation. Marpa's cushion was directly in front of me.

My eyes scanned the design on Marpa's cushion, a series of swirls set around an embroidered design of the rising sun. The colors were bright, vivid reds, greens, yellows, purples and blues, and they danced around the flaming, rising sun. I noticed, too, that there was another cushion underneath the top one, and for an instant, I had an uncontrollable urge to lift it and to see the design of the one underneath.

I lifted the cushion. Underneath was another, identical in color to the first, only instead of a series of swirls clustered about the rising sun, there was a series of straight lines that ran vertically through it. I let the cushion fall and looked about the small room again, noticing that the wall cubicles were tightly packed with rolled parchments. There was one shelf beneath the window where a number of other parchments were laid out flat, as if the guru had been working with them. I was curious but resisted the urge to go over and look at them. Instead, I closed my eyes.

Beneath closed eyelids, I saw Marpa in a thoughtful pose, looking at me. I opened my eyes again and saw that Marpa was not there. The room was empty as I had remembered it. Again, I closed my eyes and there he was. Marpa winked, then opened his eyes wide and rolled them from side to side. Startled, I again opened my eyes, and again, I found that I was alone. I closed my eyes once more.

Marpa was staring at me, shaking his great head from side to side. "Why is it that you cannot believe in me?" he asked.

I was astonished and did not try to answer.

"You do see me?" Marpa asked.

"Yes," I answered within myself, "I do see you." I was aware that, although I had answered the guru, I had not spoken out loud. My answer had come from within just as Marpa's voice came to me from within. A flutter of questions suddenly cluttered my mind.

"Good," Marpa said, smiling as if he knew my inner turmoil. "We are making progress." He paused, studying me, allowing me to compose myself. "We will take a moment and become very silent together. Be aware of the silence and what you hear within it."

My attention went immediately to the silence of the day before when I had sat with Marpa in initiation. I also recalled that when I was on the hill, thinking of Marpa, I had been aware of the musical voice of silence. I listened for it now. After a moment, I heard a soft tinkle of bells, but then the sound changed and again I heard the high-pitched sounds of the flute.

"Good," Marpa said, nodding as I tuned my attention to the thin, high-pitched sound. "Now you may journey with me into the sound itself. It will seem as if we are walking into it, and in truth, we are, although you will hear other sounds as we experience the sights there."

I had an odd feeling, as though I was stepping outside of myself, and I seemed to rise and stand next to Marpa. As though in a dream, I followed him down a long narrow trail through a deep forest, accompanied by the melodious sounds of a flute. The music was so intensely beautiful, so alluring, that the tree branches seemed moved by it, rising and falling with the swing of the melody, as if moved by a breeze, only there was no breeze. Finally, we came to the end of the forest, and we stepped into a garden of magnificent, pale yellow flowers; a translucent rainbow appeared and disappeared as the haunting melody of a peculiar pipe-like instrument produced intermittent pauses in the environment. It was breathtaking.

"Do you know where you are?" Marpa asked in a soft voice.

I did not wish to disturb the moment by speaking and so I shook my head.

"You are experiencing one of the many levels of consciousness," Marpa said. "It was the sound you heard that brought us here. Had you heard a different sound, we would have journeyed to the dimension of that sound. You followed the likeness of a flute, and it led you to this strangely beautiful place with its even keener melodies."

I listened. The music was beyond any description. It was not like the music of any village I had visited in Tibet. This music did not seem a product of physical life. Rather, as I listened and watched the effect of the music on the environment, I became aware that it was the producer of physical life. The sound, it seemed, created the environment. I had the feeling, the knowingness, that without the music there would be nothing to see; that the music manifested the scenery. I didn't know how I knew, but I knew that the celestial music was the creative power ITself.

"You have now touched on the secret of all life," Marpa said in a soft voice. "Without the melodies of silence, there can be no form."

I considered Marpa's words, listening to the strange, magical melody, and I suddenly had the urge to continue following it as I had followed the thin, high-pitched flute sound, to see where it would lead.

"Not now," Marpa said, answering my desire. "You are not yet prepared for the finer vibrations of the more subtle melodies. They are so fine that matter cannot exist in them. One must be ready for that experience. Another time."

I hesitated, wishing to go forward, drawn by the music itself.

"We must go now!" Marpa said firmly, taking me by the hand. "It is time for other experiences."

I wanted to resist, but the touch of the guru refocused my attention. There was a charge and a change of energy, a jolt, and I suddenly opened my eyes.

Marpa entered the room and sat down opposite me. He sat silently, watching the confusion on my face. After a few moments, he asked me to tell him what I had experienced. "Leave out nothing," Marpa said. "Tell me in detail everything that you have seen and felt since you entered this room."

I hesitated, remembering, then told my guru how, when I had entered the room, I had felt his presence, and how when I had closed my eyes, he had been there.

"Did nothing strike your attention in this room when you first entered?" Marpa asked.

"Oh, yes," I answered. "Everything struck my attention. The very fact that I felt your presence struck my attention. Your seat cushions struck my attention."

Marpa glanced down to the cushions he was sitting upon. "What about my cushions?" he asked.

"The designs interested me," I answered.

"You had no thoughts at the time?" Marpa questioned.

I started to answer no, but again remembered that I had been feeling the presence of the guru very strongly and that my thoughts had been of him. "I was thinking of you, my guru," I answered finally.

Marpa smiled, "I am pleased you think so well of me," he said. "It could have been a design of mad dogs or angry people ... or anything."

I was confused by Marpa's conclusion and waited for him to continue.

Suddenly, Marpa rose up on his knees and moved his large body from the cushions.

They were not the same cushions I remembered. The cushions Marpa now revealed had plain white silk covers on them. There was no design, nor any colors on them. They were pure white. Startled, I looked up to meet Marpa's gaze.

Marpa laughed at the expression on my startled face. "Do you think me a trickster?" he asked.

I did not know what to say.

"You saw a design on my cushions that was of our own making," Marpa said good-naturedly. "It is one of the great and grand powers of the mind...actually, the greatest and grandest." He paused, studying the disbelief on my face. "The grand power that I speak of has a name." He paused again, gazing steadily at me. "Its name is imagination," he said finally.

I lowered my eyes, feeling foolish.

"Stupid boy!" Marpa snapped.

I quickly looked up.

"When you brought down the hail and the wind to destroy your village enemies, how did you do it? Didn't those damned black magicians teach you anything?"

I was stunned into confusion. An image of the great and terrifying Lama Yungtun-Trogyal rushed into my mind, and I recalled how the Lama had manipulated and controlled me with his ever-changing presence. I remembered, too, that everything I had learned at the monastery was backed by some heavy emotional experience, even to the dance of illusion that I had practiced in the monastery courtyard with the monks. For all of the mock-up experiences, I could see now that the imagination had been the one all-important faculty that we used, and yet no one had ever mentioned it by name to me. No one had directly mentioned imagination. I suddenly understood. I had been taught the power of imagining, but I had never been taught the control of it. No one had ever suggested anything as simple as my deeds being a product of my imagination. I then recalled my realization that life was a dream, a succession of images passing through the mind. The images, I had discovered, were the children of imagination.

Marpa was watching me as I shifted my eyes uncomfortably under the guru's all-seeing gaze. "You have realized much since you have been in Nar, yet I can see that you have much to reconsider," Marpa said in a gentle voice. "But don't make too much out of it. Simply, the black magicians taught you to unleash the power without ever teaching you what the power was. It is the way of the evil priestcraft. If one does not know the identity of power, one cannot master it. If one can use power and not learn the mastery of it, it masters one. Then one becomes a slave of consequences, as you did." He paused, gazing at me compassionately. "But now you learn," he said kindly, "and soon you will no longer be a slave."

My eyes suddenly clouded with tears but I did not look away.

"Tell me about your discovery that life is a dream." Marpa said.

I wondered if the guru remembered that I had tried to speak with him about my discovery nearly a year ago or if he heard the passage of such thoughts through my mind. I told him that I felt that dreams came in three categories—sleeping, daydreaming, and waking experiences in life; that I felt they were all the same in that they were all part of the total destiny of an individual.

"It is true," Marpa said softly. "All dreams are made up of mind-stuff and therefore impel the direction of one's inner and outer attention, one's attitudes, one's aberrations, and the facsimiles gathered about oneself. They are filled with symbols of these attributes, which are created by the likes and dislikes of the dreamer. The dream is the experience of the mind. It tells us everything about ourselves. Sleeping dreams appear from a deeper level of mind when the body is at rest. Daydreams are memories of time past, present fantasies, and future wishes, shaped and tinted by our likes and dislikes. And so again is what we call real life. Our daily experiences are nothing more than outer reflections of the stuff we carry in mind. The world around us is nothing more than a mere reflection of our identity, and we can change it by merely changing our consciousness."

"Do you know what a miracle is, Milarepa?"

I did not speak, but waited for the guru to continue.

"A miracle is merely a changed consciousness and nothing more," Marpa said. "A miracle has nothing to do with a deity lending a helping hand to one who prays for help. There is no such thing as a helping hand. An individual finds the answers he seeks by shifting his attention from that which he seeks and, in so doing, shifts his viewpoint. His attitudes then change, and a situation that was once troublesome takes on a new appearance. Sometimes, the outcome is very dramatic and that is where the term miracle comes from." Marpa paused, a smile gradually appeared on his lips.

I smiled, too. I knew that what the guru said was true. I was filled with a sense of knowingness and the freedom that knowingness brings. Above all, I was thankful that I had stuck it out during the guru's long rejection of me.

"Finish telling me your story," Marpa said, interrupting my thought. "While the experience is fresh in your mind, tell me everything that happened before I came into the room."

I collected myself and sat up straight. I began slowly, recalling the details of how I had been curious about the open parchments but had not looked at them, and finally, the miraculous adventure with Marpa, while sitting with my eyes closed. When I had finished, Marpa unfolded his arms and held up his hands, palms up, facing me. He motioned to me to rise and led me to the open parchments on the other side of the room. I stared at them for a long moment, unaware, and then it finally dawned on me that the parchments were a dissertation on the powers of imagination.

Marpa smiled, "You may have resisted the urge to look at the parchments with your physical eyes, but your inner eyes have spent this time grasping the lessons contained in them." He paused, steadily gazing at me, as though waiting for me to grasp the realization of what had happened. It was as though a part of me had studied the scrolls, although I had never read them with my physical eyes. "Tomorrow," Marpa said, interrupting my thoughts, "you are to go with Thither to the marketplace in Nar to fill Nadar's shopping list. Not far from there, to the north, you will find a small hermitage along the banks of the narrow Rung Chu river. Stay there for few days with Thither and then return to tell me of your experiences."

CHAPTER FIFTEEN
IMPORTANT ENCOUNTERS

At daybreak, Thither and I set off for the marketplace. We took one of the guru's yaks with us to carry the empty shopping baskets that we were to fill and return to Nadar's kitchen. The air was cool, not the usual summer morning coolness, but a new coolness, which hinted the coming of autumn.

"It won't be long before the winter is upon us again," Thither said, motioning to the snow covered peaks of the higher mountains ahead.

I did not answer. I was thinking of the winter I had spent on the hill above Marpa's house, constructing the nine-story monument. We were passing beneath it, and I looked up, noticing that the leaves of the weeds around it were beginning to change color. The structure, it seemed, was not quite as large as I had remembered, although it was still an impressive sight against the early, blue-grey sky. The winter that I lived there seemed almost a dream, vague images of moving about in the cold.

"It will be my third winter with Marpa," Thither said thoughtfully. He had assumed the lead, the yak following behind him. He paused to gaze up at the edifice I had created on the hill. "It seems so long ago, doesn't it?" he said, calling back to me.

I turned around and saw that Thither had moved ahead. "Your third winter and my second," I said, hurrying to catch up.

"Yes," Thither called out, without looking back.

I moved alongside Thither. "If that is the case," I said, "then I spent nearly a year with the black magician."

Thither paused and looked at me briefly and then continued to walk. It was plain to see that he was taken by the realization of the passage of time and the marks that it had left on us. I knew that I appeared older, as he did, only I was sure that time had been more cruel to me. "And now, once again, we travel together," Thither said lightly, breaking the silence.

I was glad to be alone with him. I had missed the pleasure of his company. "Did you go directly to Nar when we parted outside the monastery?" I asked.

"Right away," Thither answered. He laughed, as though remembering. "I couldn't get away from that monastery fast enough," he said. "The place made my skin crawl. I don't know how you stood it."

"You were afraid then," I said.

Thither shook his head. "I had no purpose there," he said. "My initial reason for going there ceased to exist when I found you that night in the contemplation hall. I went there to learn something, and when I had learned it, I left."

"What had you learned?" I asked, suddenly catching my foot on a loose rock and stumbling forward. The yak made a sound behind us, as if it too had stumbled.

"I learned that while the black path contains a formula for power, it contains little understanding of that power. Those engrossed in it are more committed to the enforcement of deeds than they are in understanding the effectual cause of them."

I turned to look at Thither, catching a glimpse of the confident carriage of his head, when I stumbled again. The yak again followed my awkward footing and stumbled as well. It made a groaning sound behind us. I thought of my conversation with Marpa and remembered that the guru had made similar comments about those who practiced the black arts and that using the power and assuming it were different, separated by a fine line. I felt humbled by the fact that I had not had better sense. "Some of us learn more slowly," I said finally. "I was a slow learner."

Thither paused and turned to me. "I did not see you that way," he said. "As I saw it, you had a mission to fulfill and so you prepared for it. There are not many who could have accomplished such a task."

"There are not many who would have accomplished the destruction of a village," I said sadly.

"That is true," Thither answered.

"And now there is no purpose to my life other than that of saving my soul from the damnation it earned from those deeds," I said.

"We are all connected to each other," Thither said. He turned and continued walking.

I caught up with him. The yak snorted from behind, tugging a bit on the rope between us. "What do you mean by saying we are all connected to each other?" I asked.

Thither was silent, as if unsure of how to explain. "We are all connected, one to the other," he said again. "When one is uplifted, that one then contains the power to uplift the whole. If one is damned, then a part of all is damned. That is...I am speaking on a mass consciousness level. All the same, when you uplift someone, then you uplift yourself as an individual and as a member of the whole. You see, as individuals, we are not really separated from each other at all."

"What has that got to do with what we are discussing?" I asked, not seeing his point. Although I thought Thither's concept worth considering, it seemed far from the point of discussion.

"It has everything to do with it," Thither answered. "Your initiation was an initiation for everyone who has ever heard your name or who will ever hear your name. It was for you, personally, and for all those in the past, present, and future of your consciousness."

"I'm not sure I understand you," I said, feeling suddenly that Thither knew something about which I knew nothing at all.

"You will," Thither answered. "It is the purpose of initiation." He paused, turning to look at me. "An initiation is a fracture in an individual's hardened world. The fracture, or initiation, admits light. We live in darkness until we have earned initiation or the right to have our shells cracked open. Gradually, the fracture widens, like a split in the crust of the earth, and as it does so, the light penetrates deeper within us."

I was silent, considering Thither's words. Then I asked, "How does Marpa create the fracture you speak of?"

Thither paused along the trail again. The yak snorted gratefully behind. Thither turned to me and gazed steadily at my eyes. It was obvious that he was thinking about what he would say, carefully choosing his words. "It takes a true guru to fracture an individual's hardened world," he said thoughtfully. "First, the guru can only crack the world of an individual who is ready and willing to accept the light, which means, Milarepa, that you were both ready and willing before Marpa could give you initiation."

I considered the laborious and painful acts that finally prepared me. I had come to believe that Marpa would never accept me. I had actually given up, when suddenly the idea of making a prayer flag out of my old blanket came to mind. It was truly my only and last possession. The gift to Marpa had shown my willingness for initiation. Still, I wondered about what nature of power existed in Marpa that made initiation possible. "Where does Marpa's power to initiate come from?" I asked.

Thither hesitated, as though unsure of my question.

"How does the guru fracture a person's world? How does he admit light into it?" I asked again.

Thither searched my face, as though studying me. After a long moment, he asked if I had ever heard the music of silence.

I told him that I had, that I had become truly aware of it when I was waiting for Marpa in his chamber prior to initiation.

"The true guru uses the voice of silence to effect the fracture," Thither said. "It is actually the sound itself which, when awakened in an individual, causes the fracture. The light then follows. As I understand it, it is actually the guru, in initiation, tuning us in to the sounds of silence. After that, our constant practice of meditation and contemplation widens the fracture, until finally, all is revealed to us."

We continued in silence, not because I had no questions, but because Thither rushed ahead, dragging the yak behind him as if he was suddenly in a hurry.

I pondered Thither's comments about initiation and the sounds of silence. At the time, I had wondered if I had imagined hearing the silent sounds or if I was merely hearing Marpa's suggestion of them, but now, I realized that there was indeed a voice to silence, not one voice, but many, or at least many variations of the same voice. That was it! It was one voice which, according to Marpa's explanation, manifested differently, different sounds of it, on different planes of existence.

But what were the different planes of existence?

A low humming sound caught my attention. I paused in thought, listening to it, knowing that it was from the voice of silence, that it was a part of the silence itself. The hum reminded me of the blowing wind, whispering through the branches of the trees. Only there was no wind. The tree branches remained still and motionless and yet the sound continued, and at times, it actually seemed to increase in volume. After listening to it for some time, I realized that the voice was repeating a word, a word that seemed familiar, only I had no memory of where I would have heard it. In the humming sound of the rushing wind, I heard the word HU. It was distinct, as though it was being sung by a well-trained voice...H–UUUUUUU. Listening, I lapsed in memory and momentarily forgot where I was. Quite suddenly, I stopped walking. The yak did not see me stop in time and brushed into me, pushing me against a tree and knocking the breath out of me.

Thither turned quickly and ran to me. "Are you all right?" he asked.

I steadied myself and stood up straight. Although the HU sound had faded, I was still somewhat caught in the memory of it. I looked directly at Thither and then looked away, giving a hard but kind pat to the yak.

"The marketplace is just around the turn," Thither said. "We can continue on or we can rest here if you like."

"I am fine," I said, embarrassed by my clumsiness. "Let us continue." I laughed out loud. "If friend yak doesn't mind me bumping into him, that is."

Thither grinned and then turned around, tugging on the yak's reins as we went up over the grade. When we reached the road, we met others—men, women and children—some going to the marketplace, and some leaving it.

Rows of vegetables, meat, and livestock stalls lined the marketplace. There were also places where one could stop and eat or purchase an already prepared loaf of barley bread, or stock up on tsamba or chang beer. Nearly everyone was eating or drinking something. Even the children sucked on sweet sticks. As we paused, looking about, a child rushed up to Thither, calling out to him.

Thither stooped down, making himself eye level with the boy, who was no more than ten-or eleven-years-old. "How is your mother today?" he asked in a gentle voice. The yak was quiet and still behind him, standing next to me.

"She is not well," the boy said anxiously. "That is, she was well, and then she became sick all over again."

"Has she been smoking the root?"" Thither asked.

"She says not," the boy answered, "but I could smell it on her."

Thither looked gravely into the boy's eyes and shook his head. "There is nothing for me to do," he said. "If your mother does not want help, no one can help her."

"But she does," the boy said.

"Is that what she said?" Thither asked.

"Yes, she sent me to get you," the boy answered.

Thither rose to his feet, turned to me, and then looked down at the young boy again. "Jimilu, this is my friend Milarepa. He is another of Marpa's disciples," Thither said. Then he looked back at me. "This is Jimilu. He is the son of Nadar's grandniece. His mother has a drug addiction."

"What can you do for her?" I asked.

"Not much," Thither answered, brushing the dust from his clothes. "That which holds her captive is much more than the strength of a plant." He turned to me. "Will you wait here or will you go with me? She is here at the marketplace."

"I will go with you," I answered. I took the yak reins and followed Jimilu and Thither to the back of a vegetable stall, where a woman not much older than myself was lying on the ground, her knees doubled to her chest.

Jumilu knelt beside the woman. "The Lama Thither is here," he said, speaking softly next to her ear.

Surprised by the boy's use of the title Lama, I turned to look at my friend, but Thither showed no reaction.

"The Lama is here," the boy said again.

As though with great effort, the woman straightened her legs and rolled over on her back, gazing up into Thither's kindly face. "You have come," she said weakly.

Thither knelt down next to her. "Jimilu tells me that you are ill," he said. "What is it that troubles you?"

The woman turned her head away momentarily and then looked up at Thither again, noticing me standing above him. "Who is he?" she asked.

"A friend," Thither answered, "and also a disciple of the great guru Marpa, who sends his greeting of love and blessings to you and Jimilu."

The woman smiled, glancing up at me and then turned her attention to Thither once more. "My heart is heavy," she said. A flood of anxiety rushed to her face.

"Why?" Thither asked.

"My evil husband has stolen our yak and has threatened to murder both Jimilu and myself," she said despondently.

"Ahhh...and so his mistreatment of you has stolen your strength, as well," Thither said.

"Yes," she said, "and my spirit. He has taken it all...except my son Jimilu."

"And fortunate you are for your fine son," Thither said, putting an arm around Jimilu.

"But my husband will yet kill him...and myself," the woman said again.

"Are you so sure?" Thither asked.

"I am sure," she said.

"Then very possibly it will be so," Thither said.

"Is there nothing you can do?" she asked.

"What is it you suggest?" Thither asked. "So far, your husband has only stolen his own yak. He has not injured you or your son, or anyone else."

"But he has!" The woman insisted, rising to her elbows. "Look at me. Her appearance was disheveled and her face was smudged with dirt."

"What is it he has done to you?" Thither asked.

"He has driven me to the drug plant," the woman answered.

"Did he thrust the plant upon you with physical force, demanding that you smoke or eat it?" Thither asked.

"Good Lama, don't you understand," she said. "He has driven my spirit and made it weak and then left me."

Thither did not answer right away. Finally, he said, "Good woman, and you are a good woman, it is not your husband's harassment that threatens you, but a deep, inward craving for an ingredient of life that you cannot seem to find. You were dissatisfied with your husband and your marriage. Your business dissatisfies you, as do your friends and family, and yet your dissatisfaction has nothing to do with either those loved ones or your circumstances. As I kneel before you now, I see the apparition of a very young girl, craving for spiritual knowledge. Because the young girl felt unworthy, she did not pursue the object of her desire. She felt she could never have spiritual knowledge and so did not try for it. Instead, she married, knowing that marriage was not for her, and with it all, naturally came the dissatisfaction that crowns her now."

"I love my son," the woman said, sitting straight and defensively drawing Jimilu to her.

"Of course you do," Thither said kindly. "Your son is a manifestation of your desire to know God. Without him to care for, no doubt your weaknesses would have consumed you by now."

The woman held her son tightly to her breast. The boy did not resist. "What is it you wish me to do?" she asked Thither.

"What is it you wish to do for yourself?" Thither asked.

There was a long silence in which the woman lowered her eyes and rubbed her face in the soft hair on Jimilu's head. "I do not know," she said finally, not looking up.

"Then you must find out," Thither answered. "You must search your heart and decide." He rose to his feet. "May the blessings of my great and glorious guru Marpa be upon you," he said, and then he turned to leave.

"Wait!" the woman called out.

Thither waited but did not turn around. After a moment, when the woman did not speak again, he led me back into the open marketplace. We walked on silently for a few moments before I spoke. "You are a Lama now?"

Thither shrugged his shoulders, as if to throw off the question. "We who are on the path of knowledge are all Lamas," he said. "It is a title, nothing more. It means nothing to one on the path of truth."

I suddenly had the feeling that Thither had far surpassed me spiritually, that my own detour onto the path of the black magicians had cost more dearly than I knew. "Was there nothing you could have done to help the woman?" I asked finally.

"What would you have done?" Thither asked, returning the question.

I considered the woman before answering. If what Thither had said to her was true, that her entire life had seemed fruitless because of her unwillingness to follow spirit, then there was nothing anyone could do. Of course, Thither had said that she felt inadequate for the spiritual life, rather than unwilling to pursue it, and yet, as I thought about it, they both seemed the same. If one was truly willing, there could be no inadequacy. "But what of the boy?"

"What do you think will become of the boy?" Thither asked, again returning the question to me.

As Thither paused to purchase grains, I considered the question. Jimilu was a boy with a rare beginning. It was obvious that he would suffer greatly in his youth, as he had already done, but then, it seemed that there would also be a time when the boy's suffering would stop. He would suddenly find his own life and, I speculated, his life would be a fulfillment of what his mother had yearned for—the path of liberation. Of course, who was to say that his mother would not suddenly gain in strength and achieve it for herself?

Thither returned and hoisted a large sack of grain onto the yak's back. I moved quickly to assist him. After the sack was securely tied to the animal, Thither asked me to help him collect the other necessary supplies on Nadar's list. We led the yak hurriedly from stall to stall collecting the items, hesitating only long enough to complete each transaction and to share a bit of light-hearted conversation with the merchant. When we had finished, we purchased some tsamba, pork rind, and chang beer and sat down beneath a tree to eat and refresh ourselves. The yak grazed nearby.

"Ahhh...this is the life," Thither said, resting himself against the trunk of the tree and taking a long drink of the beer we had purchased.

I did not respond but bit off a piece of pork rind and slowly chewed it, remembering that long ago, we had shared food beneath the trees in a forest on the way to Tsang. I mused over the fact that we had been traveling together then and that we were still traveling together. It was as if our destinies were bound together in some way.

"When we are finished, let us head for the nunnery," Thither said.

"Nunnery?"

"Yes, didn't Marpa tell you?" Thither asked. "He told me that he wanted us to visit there for a few days."

"He did say there was a hermitage near the marketplace where we were to visit," I said.

"That's it. The hermitage is a nunnery," Thither said. He smiled at my surprise. "It is easier for a woman disciple to live in seclusion with other women than it is to live alone."

I understood and nodded, although it seemed strange to me that Marpa would want us to visit there.

We finished eating in silence. Thither was the first to rise. "I am ready when you are, my friend," he said. "The hermitage is not far from here, perhaps a mile to the north, along the banks of the Rung Chu."

It seemed that we had walked a very long time when, at last, the stone structures of the hermitage came into view. Thither paused on the path, turned to me, and called my attention to the residents in front of it, down by the river. We were still too far away to tell if those we saw were women. "I often wished that Marpa lived along a river bank," Thither said, looking into the distance. "The motion of a river is such a pleasurable sight."

"Perhaps it is too pleasurable," I said distantly, thinking about Nadar's grandniece and how she had escaped into drugs; how she had begged Thither for help only to be told that she must first decide what it was that she wanted help with. I didn't doubt Thither's response to the woman, but I did pity her all the same. It was a simple matter to confuse one's feelings. Right at this moment, standing with Thither and looking to the hermitage ahead, I felt a longing so great that, if I were asked suddenly to say what it was I wanted from life, I would be unable to answer.

"Is there something troubling you?" Thither asked.

"I was thinking about the woman at the marketplace and her son Jimilu," I said, merely remembering them.

"Perhaps she is also remembering us at this moment," Thither answered.

I turned to Thither questioningly.

"When you feel strong feelings for another, it is usually because the other is connecting with you...in thought waves." Thither turned back to the hermitage. "Let us go and enjoy the river," he said. He tugged at the yak's lead and started for the river.

I followed. My attention went to the boat docks on both sides of the river. There was a rope strung across, linking the two docks, and on both sides, several paddle boats were tied to a reed landing. A little further down, a rope foot-bridge crossed the river and ended at a trail on the other side that led into a large grove of pine trees. Looking about, I saw an older woman with an armload of sticks and branches moving from the forest to the dock where she loaded them onto one of the boats. When the boat was full and the cargo secure, she tugged on an overhead rope. The little boat began to move. Looking again, I saw that a woman on the hermitage side was pulling the rope connected to the loaded boat, which moved it across the river with its cargo.

The young woman tugged, and the little boat responded to every tug. In the center, where the current was the swiftest, the woman doubled her effort. I thought of hurrying ahead to help her, but the boat quickly passed the crisis point and was being drawn to shore.

"These are remarkable women," Thither said, aware that I had been ready to spring into action. "The women here do all the work that men would normally do."

"Do you know any of them?" I asked. As we neared, a few of the women waved in greeting.

"Perhaps," Thither said, unsure. "I have not been here for some months and it is rare to see the same nuns from one visit to the next."

"Why is that?" I asked.

"This nunnery is a retreat," Thither answered. "It is a place where women come to relax among other female energies. It is the old tale of like-attracts-like," he said with reserve in his voice.

"Opposites also attract," I said. I could feel my face instantly flush, and I wished that I had not said anything. I was thinking of Zesay and how she affected me.

Thither seemed to note my embarrassment. "Most nuns eventually marry ... as Nadar married Marpa," Thither added.

"Those who do not marry discover a singular way that is compatible to them."

We entered the hermitage grounds. An older woman approached us and offered to take the reins of the yak from Thither. He explained that the beast was carrying provisions for the guru Marpa and his household. The woman nodded that she understood and then led the yak to a shady spot near the river where it could drink. She tied the reins to a post.

Thither led me inside the stone and mud structure. The aroma of buttered tea filled the room. Embroidered tapestries covered the walls, and in the center of the room, was a large drum. Next to it, suspended on a golden pole, was a gong. A mallet hung on a hook next to the gong. The floors were covered with many small, plush, woven rugs. Across the room, a woman sat at a loom, weaving.

We discarded our sandals at the door before entering.

The woman looked up from her loom. She glanced at Thither and then looked directly at me. My heart raced in recognition and our eyes locked in greeting.

It was Zesay.

I dared not move or speak for fear that her image would dissolve. I even tried not to look directly at her, so that, if she was a product of my imagination, I could hold her before me as long as possible.

Zesay was older but still beautiful. The flush of youthful innocence had faded from her cheeks, but there was still a sparkle in her eyes, and as she grew accustomed to seeing me there, the same faint touch of a smile gently lifted the corners of her mouth. It was a smile that was so delicate that I cautioned myself to keep my thoughts clear so as not to disturb the grace of the moment. She rose from her seat at the loom and turned to me with a slight but perfect bow. I returned the greeting.

"Zesay," I said, feeling a rise of emotion as I said her name. I was near enough to see that she felt the emotional swell, as well. Her eyes were suddenly shining and full.

"Mila," she said softly. "Is it really you?"

No one but Zesay and my sister Peta ever called me by the shortened version of my name. My eyes suddenly filled in response, but I did not look away. It was so long since we had seen each other that I could not bear to move my eyes from her now.

"I knew I would see you again," she said.

I found that I could not speak. Scores of feelings were rising in me, and each time I would try to voice one of them, another would crowd it out. There was nothing for me to do but remain silent and to absorb the finest detail of my beloved Zesay.

Zesay turned to Thither who had been patiently watching the interaction. Not being from our village, he had not known Zesay, although he had often heard of her from me. "Will you excuse us?" Zesay asked politely.

"Of course, Lomas," Thither said, casting a glance at me.

"Please be at home and at peace here," Zesay said to him.

"Thank you, I will," Thither answered. He bowed and, without looking back, turned and left the building.

I watched the graceful movements of my beloved, and I was aware of her poise in asking Thither to allow us privacy. I was also aware that Thither had called Zesay Lomas, which was the title of one in authority.

Zesay came to me, took me by the hand, and led me to a sitting area on the plush carpets in a far corner of the room. "Please, sit down," she said softly.

I sat down and watched as Zesay took two cups and went to a small black pot and poured the thick buttered tea into the cups. I remembered that the scent of the tea had struck me upon first entering the room with Thither, and taking the cup from her, I waited until she had seated herself across from me before drinking.

"You have become a hermit?" I asked.

Zesay nodded. The response was reserved.

"How long have you lived this way?" I asked.

Since shortly after you left Nyang, she said. She hesitated before she added, "I was not in the village when the destruction occurred."

I lowered my eyes.

"You did what you had to do," Zesay said kindly, "or at least what you believed you had to do. It is over now, and I can see that the path you travel is the right one for you."

I lifted my head and looked into her eyes again. She seemed to grow more beautiful by the moment, and I could barely resist the urge to reach out and take her into my arms.

"Tell me about your travels...please," she asked. There was a slightly pleading tone to her voice. "So many times, I was sure that I was with you. At times, I could feel your pain...at times, the pain was unfathomable agony. On one occasion, I felt that you were alone and lost, wandering through the mountains without food, drink or clothing. There seemed no doubt that you were near death." She paused, studying the changing expressions on my face. "I prayed that you would not die just then. My fear was not for your death but for the damnation that hovered over you."

I closed my eyes and opened them again, gazing into the depths of her wondrous being. "You did not know about Nyang?" I asked.

"Not until much later," she said.

"If it had not been for the image of you that came to me in the depth of my hell, I might have succumbed to the damnation I well deserved." I paused, drew in a deep breath, and then continued. "But, beloved, as you were looking at me in your mind's eyes, I was also looking at you. Sometimes, I would remember things you had said to me, and sometimes, I remembered nothing but you, your dear, sweet, beloved face. I remembered only that I loved you." I paused. "I love you now more than all of life."

She lowered her eyes and sipped her tea, and when at last she looked up again, her breathing was even. She was poised and controlled. "Our love is no mere love," she said warmly. "Our love contains all of the ingredients of perfected love. It is whole and complete in itself."

I studied the calm expression on Zesay's face. Although she appeared warm and loving, she was also strong and detached. She had spoken words of love, and while I knew them to come from her heart, I also knew that there would be no love-making to express them. A part of me wanted to run from the pain of that realization, and another part accepted it without reservation.

"Do you remember the Lama Kataka?" she asked.

I nodded, looking deeply into her. "Mostly, I remember him through you and what you told me of him," I said.

"After you left for Tsang, I could no longer continue a life in Nyang," Zesay said. "Everything reminded me of you and how much I missed you. I became reclusive in my loneliness. I knew that you could never return for me." She paused, taking a sip of tea. She looked at me again. "Lama Kataka suggested that it was time for me to decide on my purpose in life and to follow that decision."

"I gave my future a great deal of consideration. Since I knew that I could never marry, I turned my attention inward. I became a full-time student of the spiritual life." Zesay paused, smiling. "I have not regretted that decision," she said.

I sat motionless, looking at her for a long while before speaking. "Can you share with me what you have learned?" I asked.

Zesay slowly drew in a deep breath, held it, and slowly exhaled again. "In a nutshell, I have learned that all life is spiritual, that there is nothing that is not of a spiritual nature."

I stared at her for a moment before responding. "That is a pretty saying, but I am not sure of its truth," I said, remembering my revenge upon Nyang. "Would you say that my evil deeds were of a spiritual nature?"

"Yes," Zesay said, "even that. The spiritual life views things not as good or bad, but as experiences. When one realizes his experiences for what they are, one then understands the nature of them. Your deeds were evil, but nevertheless, they provided you with an opportunity to rise above evil. Because you committed evil, you no longer wish to commit it. I am sure you have also come to understand that many threads were used to weave the tapestry of your deeds. The tapestry was, in part, woven by your family and your circumstances at birth."

I gazed deeply at Zesay. For an instant, I had the feeling that I was sitting with her in the kitchen of her mother's home as I had done so many times in the past. "And what would you say about the murderer or thief who does not yet regret his deeds? I asked."

"I would say that he does not yet recognize that his deeds are merely experiences like any experience, to be moved through and put aside, to be used as a tool to understand the true nature of self." Zesay did not move as she waited for me to respond. When I did not speak, she continued. "The person who recognizes the true nature of experience has lived many, many lifetimes. Becoming aware of the environment, the true nature of it, the true nature of ourselves, is a very slow process which requires many lifetimes."

The repetition of Zesay's words were echoed again in the silent recesses of my mind.

"I live as a hermit, not because it is a holy way to live, but because it no longer benefits me to live a life of distractions," she said. "Now I walk into many villages, and I talk with the people there, but I am not one of them. I can be with them, but I am not of them." She stopped and looked around the room. "This is only a room arranged by destiny as a meeting place." She paused and smiled.

"Marpa told me to come here," I said, uncertain of what she meant. "Marpa told me to come to this hermitage and then return to tell him what I had learned. I wonder if he knew that I would meet you here?"

"Perhaps he sensed that an important encounter awaited you here," Zesay said. "A guru is always mindful of the quality of experiences his disciple has."

"You speak like a guru yourself," I said.

Zesay grinned. "No, but I have had one long enough to know how they operate," she said.

"Is it still Kataka?" I asked.

"Yes," she answered.

"He is well, I hope," I said politely.

"Yes, although he is still in Nyang," Zesay said.

I lowered my eyes and raised them again. "You have not seen him since the destruction?" I asked.

"A true disciple never loses sight of the guru," Zesay answered.

I nodded that I understood. I recounted my meeting with Marpa and how the guru had shaped me through manual work, building stone house after stone house and tearing them all down, until the final one. I laughed out loud when I told Zesay about the nine-story monument, and I cried when I told her of the prayer flag I made for my initiation gift. When finally all was said, I held out my hand to her.

Zesay placed her hand in mine. "Let me show you around the place," she said, rising to her feet and pulling me up with her. "Do you remember how, as children, we wished to play near a river?"

We went out of the building and into the outdoors. It was then that I became aware of the heavy pine scent in the air. I looked to the forest on the other side of the river and motioned toward it. Zesay slipped her hand from mine, and we walked slowly to the river's edge.

CHAPTER SIXTEEN
THE TRICK

The high, thin, sparkling air of the mountains danced in the afternoon sunlight, cascading on the wavy surface of the river. I did not know when I had ever been so happy. The river, it seemed, had joined its life with the life of the sunlight, and when suddenly I turned to Zesay, I saw that she too was caught in the light, joined to the river by it and to me, as well. The light shone through her and between us, and when Zesay smiled, I sensed the light was coming from inside her.

I lightly touched her hand, my fingers brushing against hers as we walked side by side. It was a sweet encounter, but tinged with the pain of restraint. I hesitated before touching her again, and when I did, it was again sweet but painful. This time, she turned to face me.

"Our paths have merged for a short while," she said, taking a step away from me. "There is a purpose to our meeting."

I gazed at Zesay's clear, dark eyes, trying to catch a glimpse of the purpose she mentioned. I could barely contain the passion that was mounting in me.

She turned her head and looked downstream, pointing to the footbridge across the river. "Let us cross," she said, "I know a special place."

"A special place." I rolled her words over and over again in my thoughts as I followed her. She moved quickly along the river bank, nodding to the other women as we passed. When we reached the footbridge, she hurried ahead with accustomed quickness, holding tightly to the ropes as she crossed. Once or twice, she glanced back at me. Her expression was unsmiling and serene, and her eyes flashed with purpose.

When we reached the other side, she paused and pointed to a trail through the pine trees and then led me along it. We walked for what seemed to be an endless time. Finally, we came to a clearing, and she stopped in the middle of it. It was not a large clearing but an opening in the thick pine grove. Tall blades of grass grew up through a bed of pine needles. Zesay looked at me and then pointed up through the opening of the trees.

I leaned my head back and looked up. Rays of sunlight brushed against my cheeks. In the rush of warmth, I quickly looked down to see Zesay also bathed in light.

"This is one of the sun's flowering spots," Zesay said, watching me. "Do you know now why I brought you here, Mila?"

I swallowed, trying to ease the dryness in my throat. I did not answer her. I did not even dare to try.

"Give me your hand," she said softly.

I slowly extended my hand. A painful sensation rushed up my arm as she clasped her fingers about mine.

"Mila, you must relax," Zesay said. She sat down on the ground and pulled me down next to her. Then she gently pushed my chest down so that I was lying on my back. While she sat next to me, her fingers touched my eyes lightly, closing them. "With your eyes closed, feel the warmth of the sun upon you," she said softly, "and relax, Mila." She moved her hand away.

I could not bear the loss of her touch. "Please, come next to me, Zesay," I whispered, looking up at her with half-opened eyes. The glare from the sun made it seem as if the light were passing directly through her. Her hair, forehead, nose, and chin were touched by it, glistening.

Zesay touched my brow with her hand. The cool, sensuous touch of her hand on my face made my breath catch, and as she brought her lips down to mine, there was a split second of darkness, and then again, a flash of light. We had drawn together and turned until both of us shared the light. It was there, in the heat of the day, that we joined in love.

"Mila, I had a reason for telling you that this was a special place," Zesay said, straightening her hair. She smiled down at me. "It was not entirely for making love."

I rose up on my elbows and gazed at her, noting how very beautiful she was, even now in the fading sunlight.

She adjusted her skirt and rose to her feet. "There is something I must show you," she said, reaching a hand down for me.

I took her hand and rose to my feet as well. A surge of strength rushed into me. I pulled her to me.

"Mila," she said, firmly pushing me from her. "We are no mere lovers."

I knew what she said was true. I did not feel ordinary in her presence. "Being with you is all that I want," I answered.

She shook her head slowly from side to side. "Our time has passed," she said. She glanced to the ground where we had loved. "We were given a moment to fulfill our vows, nothing more."

I drew her to me. "What do you mean?" I asked, holding her hands firmly in mine, waiting for an explanation.

"I asked you here, to this special place, knowing that we would make love, but not merely for that purpose."

"Not for that purpose," I repeated.

She shook her head.

"What purpose then?"

"Close your eyes," she said

"Zesay...please!"

"It is important," Zesay said again.

I closed my eyes.

"Now, take my hand."

I took her hand.

Zesay led me through the pine forest. We had not gone far when she stopped and lifted my hand to her face. "Now, my love," she said, "open your eyes."

For a split second, I did not know what it was that I was seeing. Zesay, I knew, was in front of me, and yet, I could not see her. Instead, I saw an aura of sparkling lights, each one a tiny fraction of another, greater light. Gradually, the vision cleared, and I saw Zesay again. She was standing on a rock, no more than an arm's length away, pointing to a cliff in the opposite direction. I turned to look.

On the cliff wall was Zesay's face. It was not a drawn image of her, but her actual face. Astonished, I turned to the rock where I had last seen her. She was still there, still pointing to the cliff. Again, I turned to the cliff, and again, I saw her face. I saw her from the neck up and she was smiling at me.

"It's a trick," Zesay said.

I saw the face in the cliff speak, and I quickly turned again to the rock where I had seen Zesay standing. She was still there.

"It's a trick," she said again.

"I can see that," I said. I turned and walked over to the cliff and touched the image of Zesay's face, only it was not her flesh I was touching but a rock wall. For an instant, I recalled images on a wall in the prayer room at the Lama Yungtun-Trogyal's monastery. "Zesay," I said, turning to her, "do we have to do this?"

Zesay did not answer.

I went over to the rock where she was standing.

"Look," she said, pointing to the cliff again.

I turned to the cliff to see her face fade and then turned back to where she was standing on the rock. She was watching me.

"Aren't you curious?" she asked.

I shook my head from side to side. "You forget my lineage," I said. "Did you think I learned nothing from the black magician?"

She did not answer, but stood silently watching me.

"Marpa calls me the great sorcerer," I said scornfully. "He calls me that because, in some areas of knowledge, I cannot yet seem to help myself. Things happen as a result of my powers. I am now learning to exercise control over my feelings."

Zesay stepped off the rock and suddenly began laughing.

"You make fun of my burden," I said. I had the feeling that she was mocking me.

"Mila, my dearest, I do not mock you. I mock the false set of rules that bind you."

"What do you mean?"

"I showed you a trick," Zesay said, "and, because you already knew something of the trick, you negated its value. Immediately, you tell me that you know of it and cast it aside as sorcerer's knowledge."

"But it is sorcerer's knowledge," I said firmly.

"I did not study with the black magician," Zesay said. "The trick I showed you was one I learned in contemplation. It was a gift to me for the effort I put forth. It was a gift to me from myself." She paused, studying me. "Remember, I told you, all of life is spiritual?"

"I remember those words, yes," I answered, not at all sure that I agreed.

"It is true," she said. "All life is spiritual...even the tricks of illusions we conjure. It is the intention behind one's deeds that makes the deed good or bad." She paused again.

I did not speak or show any change in expression.

"How did you learn to wreck a village?" she asked.

I lowered my eyes and turned away from her.

She let out a sigh. "Mila, it is not my intention to hurt you. I did not bring up the subject of your deeds to make you feel badly for them. That is over now. Now, you must look at your past as a useful tool."

I turned to face her. "What are you saying?" I demanded.

Zesay hesitated, as though trying to find the right way to explain. "I have learned that the light body within one's self can be reflected," she said, finally. "It all has to do with the divine force or divine energy that flows through us. Once understood, our presence can be reflected in such a way that we appear to be in our physical bodies in more than one place at a time."

"But you said it was a trick," I said.

"Well, it is," Zesay answered. "It is a trick and yet it is real." She paused, studying the uncertainty on my face. "It does not really have to be done in this special place either."

"Then why did you bring me here?" I asked.

Zesay gazed lovingly into my eyes.

I could feel the rush of blood to my face as she gazed upon me and, warmed by her eyes, I lifted her hand to my lips.

"This is the place where I discovered the trick," she said, "and yet people who are not aware that they do it unconsciously all the time call it a trick when someone draws their attention to it."

I was thoughtful. "I don't understand," I said. "Do you mean that everyone reflects themselves in the manner that you did?"

Zesay nodded. "To some degree," she said. "Reflecting one's image begins with a strong thought. The thought travels to the point imagined. When one becomes aware of doing this, one begins to become aware of another kind of travel, a travel beyond thought."

"And what would that be?" I asked, amazed.

"The travel or reflection of Consciousness," Zesay answered.

I lowered my eyes thoughtfully and then raised them again. Zesay was watching me, and I felt the warm glow of her love. "Are you saying that the Zesay I saw on the cliff was Zesay's Consciousness?" I asked.

She nodded. "Something like that," she said. "It was a Consciousness reflection that you saw, just as it was a Consciousness reflection that you saw standing on the rock, pointing to the cliff."

I was struck by her words and stood gazing at her, wondering what she meant. She had said that the image of her on the wall was a reflection, as was the image of her pointing to her image on the rock wall. If that was true, if both were reflections, then what was she now? Was she still a reflection? I was touching her, holding her hand. Was I touching a reflection? Had I indeed made love with a reflection?

She drew in a long breath, held it, and exhaled slowly. "Mila, although we are sharing this meeting in the reflective state, we are still together," she said softly.

"What do you mean WE?" I asked.

"Is it so difficult for you to accept?" she asked sadly.

"What?"

"You saw my image reflected on the wall," Zesay said.

"Yes."

"The image you see before you now is also a reflection," Zesay said. "I am a reflection of my physical form, just as you are."

I stared at her, uncertain of what she was saying.

"We are here in the forest outside the hermitage," Zesay said again, "but we are not here. Our physical bodies are not here, only the ethereal forms of them."

"But we made love," I said, with certainty in my voice.

"Yes, we did, and it may be that we will love again in that way...or we may not."

"I don't believe you," I said. "We are here, truly here." I paused, squeezing her fingers between the palms of my hands. "I can feel your hand in mine."

Zesay nodded.

I was suddenly afraid to speak, fearing that something I would say would make her disappear. I squeezed her hand tightly between mine.

"Don't you see," Zesay said, "that every time you have thought of me, I have thought of you? We are bound together by love, although that is not the only emotion that binds one to another. We are here together for these moments because the love between us is so strong."

"If your physical body is not here, then where is it?" I asked, finding it difficult to speak.

"It makes no difference, nor does it make a difference as to how far away my physical body is," Zesay answered. "It is no different. Consciousness knows no distance."

I hesitated, trying to control the panic that was rising in me. "Where am I?" I managed to ask. "If I am not here, then where am I?"

I felt a sudden and terrible jolt, as though someone or some force was shaking me. My vision was blurred, and Zesay seemed to shimmer before me and then disappear. Too shaken to think, I closed my eyes and lowered my head. I was nauseous and dizzy and felt that I might black out.

"Are you all right, Milarepa?" a voice said next to me.

I hesitated, confused, realizing the pitch and texture of the words to be unlike Zesay's voice. Slowly, I lifted my head and opened my eyes. Thither stood next to me, while in front of me, instead of Zesay, was a much older woman. She gazed at me questioningly. "Where is Zesay?" I asked.

The woman shook her head, looking from me to Thither. "I know no one by the name of Zesay," she said, calmly.

I swooned. Thither caught me by the arm and held me up. "Excuse us, Lomas," he said to the nun, and then helping me to stand, he turned me around and led me out of the room.

Thither led me inside a small hut. It was a brightly carpeted room with two small windows. As though in a dream, I turned and looked about the tiny space and then lay down on a fleece that Thither had placed along the wall.

Thither sat down next to me. "What did you experience in there, standing before the Lomas?" he asked.

I gazed into Thither's kindly face, remembering. "The Lomas," I said hesitantly, "she was Zesay."

"She looks like Zesay?" Thither asked.

"No," I answered, hesitating again. "The woman did not look like Zesay. Zesay was there. It was Zesay, not the old woman, who greeted us."

Thither sat gazing at me without speaking for a long while. Finally, he said, "It appears you have an experience to share with Marpa. I would suggest you hold it to yourself until then, clearing the details in your mind, so that whatever it was you experienced does not become distorted by careless chatter."

I searched my friend's face and saw the understanding there. I sensed that Thither had had his share of unusual experiences.

"You do not have to wait until our return to speak to the guru," Thither said. "Simply imagine Marpa's image before you. Speak to him as plainly as you would if you were together. He will listen to you." Then he rose to his feet, saying that he would attend to the yak, and left me alone.

I tried to calm myself and to contemplate the image of the guru Marpa. I remembered sitting alone in the guru's chambers and how I felt his presence as I waited for him to join me prior to my initiation, and I remembered hearing the music of the silence. The memory seemed to overlap the present moment in an easy, natural way, and I was not surprised when I saw Marpa sitting before me.

"Tell me what you have experienced since you left my house," the guru instructed.

I hesitated, suddenly stunned by realization that Marpa's image appeared genuine, and I became tangled in a maze of mental argument. Frustrated by my confusion, I opened my eyes.

The image of Marpa was gone. The music of silence was gone, as well. I arose and walked across the carpeted floor of the little hut to the door and stepped outside. Looking about, I saw

Thither down at the river's edge with the yak. The smell of tsamba and sweetbreads and buttered tea was in the air. Although everything appeared quite normal and at ease, I knew that something very special was happening to me. Even though I could not see them, I knew both Zesay and Marpa were there, looking at me.

CHAPTER SEVENTEEN
THE RECLAMATION

Thither spoke very little on our return trip to Marpa's house, and I was grateful for the silence. I was filled with memories of Zesay and I sensed that, if I talked about them, their existence would dissipate, and I could not bear to forfeit one instant of my memory with her. I stayed in the background, behind Thither and the yak.

Toward nightfall, we arrived at Marpa's house. A candle had already been lit and placed in the kitchen window. Nadar worked busily in the kitchen, moving back and forth to the cooking pot. There seemed to be a silhouette of someone else in the background, and because of the slimness of the individual, I knew that it was not Marpa.

Thither let out a shrill whistle to signal our arrival. Nadar rushed to the window and looked out, waving in greeting. Thither waved back. I watched, feeling oddly, as though once again I was dreaming.

Thither tied the yak to the tree in front of the house and began to unload the supplies from it. I hurried to help.

"Are you all right?" he asked, staying my hand from reaching for the heavy bundles.

I nodded and reached for a sack of grain, but again, his hand intercepted mine. "Relax," he said, "I'll carry them into the house. You take the yak to the stable and feed him."

I glanced at my friend's face and nodded gratefully. I had dreaded going into the house and facing Nadar and possibly Marpa and a guest at this time. I would feed and care for the yak and then slip in through the back way.

When Thither had finished unloading the beast, I untied it and gave a gentle tug on the rope. Relieved of its burden, the animal shook itself and followed me to the stable in the back of the house.

The stable was draped in semi-darkness, and I paused before entering, noticing that the other animals were undisturbed, and then led the yak inside to its place alongside the feed bin. The yak snorted and then made a soft cooing sound, exhaling through closed lips, as I placed the feed at its head. I paused and watched it eat.

The beast ate slowly, savoring every bite, occasionally swishing a fly with its tail. Observing it, I had the feeling I was observing a bit of myself, that a part of me was moving slowly, contemplatively savoring every little memory of my time with Zesay. I did not care if it had been an illusion.

"Are you so preoccupied that you have forgotten me?" a man's voice said from behind.

Startled, I spun on my heels. A man appeared to be standing in the deep shadow at the far end of the stable. I recalled the silhouette of a stranger in Nadar's kitchen.

"Surely, you remember me," the voice said.

A slow, icy feeling crept up my back and settled at the base of my neck, making my skin prickle. It was Narquin from the black magician's monastery! Had he been waiting for me in Marpa's house?

"We have been waiting for you to return," Narquin said. He stepped from the shadows into the lighted doorway. The fading sun hovered at his back, creating an even more eerie effect on the front of him.

Filled with terror, I could not speak or move.

"Did you think that we would not meet again?" Narquin asked.

I did not know and did not try to answer. I had hoped that that part of my life was over, that the man before me was an illusion.

"You are more than a year overdue," Narquin said. "The Lama Yungtun-Trogyal was concerned and sent me to bring you back."

I fought for inner control, recalling that Narquin had instructed me to return quickly to the monastery following the destruction of my village. He had warned me that my failure to return would result in dire consequences. I had since learned why I had been cautioned. By my usage of power, I had claimed it. My every thought, word, and action was now filled with power. It was how I had poisoned Marpa's drinking well by merely cursing it. I recalled how Marpa had made me drink my own poison and how it had nearly cost me my life.

"You live through the grace of your present guru," Narquin said, "but still, the past is about you."

"In what way?" I blurted out. A tremor began in my body, rising from my feet, as I dreaded the answer.

Narquin glared at me. "Nyang still suffers from your blows," he said easily. "As long as the village suffers, you will be remembered as the cause of it. Even beyond the suffering, the people of Nyang will compose songs about the terrible legendary demon named Milarepa who cursed them." He paused, drawing in a deep breath and exhaling slowly. "Your deeds have made you immortal, Milarepa. You cannot escape them. They follow you everywhere. They fill the heart of every man you meet. You are no longer free, and you bind others by your presence." Narquin paused, watching me. "You must return to the monastery," he said.

My body was now visibly shaking, and as I tried to shake my head to answer no, the movement was not well defined. "I will not return," I said in an unsteady voice. "I have found another way, a way to save myself."

Narquin threw up his hands. "It cannot be!" he said dramatically. "You have the power. Whatever you think, feel, or even touch becomes tainted by your existence."

"I am also acquiring control of the power," I blurted out. "No longer do I offend others by my thoughts and speech." A wave of nausea filled me.

Narquin calmly watched me. "Surely you can see what is now happening to you, Milarepa," he said. "You look at me with terror, because I am a symbol of the terror that you once spread among others. That terror now sickens you." Narquin paused, then added, "It will consume you."

A sharp, uncontrollable pain drew me sideways, and I doubled over; my stomach retched as a thick, dark fluid spurted from my mouth.

"Time is running out for you," Narquin said. "Come with me now. Come and free yourself from this misery."

I tightly closed my eyes in an effort to resist and, trying not to slip into unconsciousness, I silently called out to Marpa, inwardly pleading with the guru for assistance.

It seemed that instantly there was movement nearby and, with my peripheral vision, I saw Marpa enter the stable and stand next to me.

"Get up, Milarepa. Get up!"

I opened my eyes, turned my head and looked into the guru's face.

"Get up," Marpa demanded. "You will disturb the house if you come in much later."

As I gazed into the face above me, I was suddenly aware that it was not Marpa at all, that it was his wife Nadar. Shocked into well being, I rose to my feet and stared at the woman. "I believed I saw Marpa here," I said.

"Probably," the woman answered. "Anyway, he sent me to fetch you." Seeing the alarm on my face, she added, "but don't tell him I told you." She hesitated. "I was getting ready for bed and suddenly Marpa said to me, "Go into the stable and tell Milarepa to come into the house!" I said to him, "Why don't you do it yourself?" Nadar paused again, as if to see if I was following her. Marpa said, "You get him, because if I do, it will ruin everything." "And so, here I am," Nadar said.

"Was Marpa here?" I prodded.

"If you saw him, he was," Nadar said, smiling. "Just because you don't see him doesn't mean that he isn't here. Marpa is no mere man," she said emphatically. "And now that you are initiated, there is a mighty bond between you."

I felt calmed by the presence of the woman before me. I had never given Nadar credit for being anything more than Marpa's wife, but now I saw that Nadar was a remarkable person in her own right.

"Come on," she said, moving to the door. "It is time we were all in bed."

I started to follow her and then stopped. Narquin was standing in the center of the doorway. Nadar did not seem to notice.

"Come on," Nadar said, reaching a hand back to me.

I took the woman's hand and followed her. Narquin stepped aside as we passed through the doorway.

It was not quite dawn when Nadar woke me, standing over my bed, gently shaking me. I had been in a deep sleep and was therefore slow to open my eyes. When I did and saw Nadar's kindly face there, I smiled.

"Marpa wants you," Nadar said softly. "You must hurry. Already he is in his study waiting for you." She handed me a piece of jerky and a small bundle of tsamba. "Eat while you dress," she said, "so that you will not be delayed."

When Nadar left, I quickly rose from my fleece and stretched. Memory flashes of the night before came rushing in on me and I turned suddenly and looked about the room. There was no one there. I dressed myself, took an occasional bite of the food Nadar had left, and stuffed the remaining amount in the lining of my robe, hurrying out the doorway to Marpa's office.

Marpa was seated on a high rise of cushions next to the wall where he always sat. He looked up the instant I appeared in the doorway.

"Let's get to work," he said, motioning to the cushions across from him. "Be seated. We have much to accomplish this day."

I bowed and hurried to the vacant cushions and sat down, folding my legs in front of me. I did not take my eyes off Marpa.

"Tell me of your journey," Marpa said, tucking his hands into his sleeves and folding his arms. He looked directly at me.

"Last night," I began, remembering Narquin's visit.

"No! Do not begin with last night. Begin at the beginning, when you first began the journey with Thither."

I thought of the hermitage and of Zesay.

"No!" Marpa said again, as if aware of my thought, "begin at the beginning."

"The marketplace?" I asked.

"Before that. What happened when you left here with Thither?" Marpa asked. "Recount the entire journey to me."

I hesitated, trying to recall the details of my journey with Thither. I remembered that we had shared the same feelings of friendship as on our journey to the monastery of the black magician some years ago, and I related these feelings to Marpa. I paused, filling in the spaces with memories of things Thither had said, marveling at the wisdom Thither had acquired and the fact that I felt he was so far ahead of me in understanding the higher principles.

"Did you speak of your initiation?" Marpa asked.

"No," I answered.

"Are you sure?"

I was thoughtful. Thither had brought it up. He had asked me if I knew how the guru initiated, and then explained how a guru fractures the initiate's world and admits light into it, using the voice of silence to effect the fracture. When I had finished recounting these details to Marpa, I hesitated, looking deeply into the guru's eyes. For an instant, I felt I was flying, soaring out of and above my body. The sensation was exhilarating, and I remembered that while Thither told me of initiation, I had felt the same exhilaration, and that there had been feelings of the guru's presence while he spoke. Had Marpa been with us in unseen presence?

Marpa smiled, again as if he heard my thoughts. "Go on with your story," he said.

"Then I heard the music of silence," I said, remembering. "I was captivated by it." I hesitated.

"Then what happened?" Marpa prodded.

I recounted how, for a moment, I had forgotten myself and what was going on around me and that the yak then accidentally stumbled into me, knocking the breath out of me.

"There is no such thing as an accident," Marpa said.

"But it was an accident," I said defensively.

Marpa shook his head. "Accidents do not exist. The word accident is an excuse invented by man to avoid facing up to the cause of an incident." He paused, studying me. "In your case, the cause was split attention. You were trying to move about in the physical world with your attention in the worlds of Consciousness. You are not yet capable of doing both at the same time."

"Accidents and misfortune go hand in hand for the average man who does not understand spiritual law. In truth," Marpa said, pausing again, "accidents and misfortune are mere reflections of a person's attention. The quality of one's attention is the determining factor of the outcome. A person who holds his attention on negative thoughts will draw circumstances to himself according to the intensity of his thoughts."

"But I was not thinking in a negative way," I said.

"You still carry the mind passions," Marpa answered. "You are still filled with anger." He paused.

I recalled how Zesay had once remarked that I was easily angered.

"It is only one of the passions that hold you," Marpa said.

"But I was not angry at the time. I was listening to the music of the spheres. There was nothing angry or negative in my thoughts." I paused, thinking back to the time when the yak accidentally knocked me against the tree.

"Whether you held those thoughts at the moment or not, anger still binds you," Marpa said firmly. "As long as anger or any of the other passions of mind can touch you – lust, greed, vanity, or attachment – you are a mere puppet of the negative forces. As their grip begins to loosen from you, accidents will occur less frequently and your direction from Consciousness will be heightened. Gradually, you will be able to focus on the higher quality of things and still move about in the physical world without injury." He paused. "Now, go on with your story," he said.

I then told Marpa of the marketplace and how the child Jimilu had called on Thither to visit his mother who was a drug addict. When I had finished, I waited for Marpa to comment.

"Did you disagree with Thither's manner of handling the situation?" Marpa asked.

Remembering, I thoughtfully shook my head. "Thither's judgment was compassionate but detached, and I understood and respected him for it."

"Good," Marpa said, searching my face. "But there is something you have not said about the incident."

I raised my eyes to Marpa's. There seemed to be nothing that the guru did not know about me. "It was Jimilu," I said finally.

"What about him?" Marpa asked.

"He seemed such a pure and special boy," I answered. "I felt strongly protective, wishing him no harm. There was a moment, when I looked into the boy's eyes, that I believed I recognized him, as though we had met before, and that in some way we were bound together." I hesitated. "I know that sounds foolish," I concluded.

Marpa gazed deeply into my eyes but did not speak. After some time had passed, he asked me to continue telling the story of my journey.

I told Marpa of how we had gone to the hermitage by the river, how we had entered a building where I was surprised to find Zesay, sitting at a weaving loom. I also told him that Thither had left us alone and that Zesay and I had walked out by the river and had crossed the bridge to the other side. When I came to the part of our joining in the sun spot, I paused to see Marpa's reaction, but the guru was listening with his eyes closed and merely nodded for me to continue.

I told Marpa of my lovemaking with Zesay and then how she had taken me to what she called a special place, where she reflected her image onto a nearby cliff. "She had tried to explain the reflection to me as a means of Consciousness travel, but I was more interested in being with her and would not pay attention." I then told him of Zesay's disappearance, and how, in my anxiety, I had called upon the guru for understanding, and how, at first, I believed I saw the guru and then, shocked by what I was seeing, the guru, too, had seemed to disappear.

"That is enough," Marpa said slowly, opening his eyes and looking at me. "Can you see now how you were affected by your mind?"

Uncertain, I did not answer.

"Did you not say that, while contemplating, your communication with me was cut off by other thoughts that crowded your mind?" Marpa asked.

I nodded.

"And did you not say that, while Zesay was trying to explain Consciousness travel to you, you thought only of a life with her?"

"Yes," I said, still uncertain of his point.

"Can you not see what you have done?" Marpa asked impatiently.

Caught by the guru's tone of voice, I could not concentrate on the question.

"Mila," the guru said, gently speaking my boyhood name. "Listen to me. This is Marpa, your guru, sitting in front of you. I am trying to show you something of great importance but you must listen, not to the wanderings of your mind, but to me. Listen to me, Mila."

I was again caught by the guru's tone of voice. It amazed me that at first the guru had appeared impatient and now he treated me lovingly, as a father.

"Do not listen with your ears, Milarepa. Listen with your heart. A voice can trick you. As you can see, I am neither displeased nor pleased with you, and yet, because you have been listening with your ears, you have been deceived by a tone of voice." He paused, watching me.

"Milarepa!" Marpa suddenly shouted, leaning forward on his cushions so that his face was inches from my own.

Startled, I jumped, my eyes looking directly into his.

"Milarepa, you must take control of your mind. Right now, your mind controls you. It is your master. When you take control of it, you will become its master. Then you will have the power to live in the present moment. You will be able to be with your guru at any time, at any place, completely undisturbed. You will also be able to be with Zesay at any time, at any place, completely undisturbed." He paused, watching the expression change on my face. "Do you understand me?" he asked.

"Yes, my guru," I said, bowing while seated before him. I was aware that my body responded with unexpected enthusiasm at his reference to Zesay. "What must I do to gain control of myself?"

Marpa gazed deeply into me for a long time before answering. "Do you, as yet, understand why you were visited by Narquin last night?"

I was hesitant, aware that I had all but forgotten Narquin's confrontation. Now that I was reminded of it, the same uneasy feeling crept through me. I looked around the small room, expecting him to be there, relieved that I was still alone with Marpa. "I must still be poisoned by my guilt," I answered, finally.

"It is your mind that poisons you," Marpa said. "Your mind made it possible for Narquin to visit you. If you had control of your mind, if you had been master over it, Narquin could not visit unless he was invited to do so."

"How do I take control of my mind?" I asked.

"By examining your attitudes," Marpa said. "Your attitudes are your viewpoints of life. They are the anchorpoints of your consciousness. You must first discover what they are before you can deal with them." He paused, watching as I moved uncomfortably on the cushions in front of him. "Today is a holiday for you. Refresh yourself with food, drink, and rest. Tomorrow, I will take you to Echo Cave where you can contemplate your attitudes. It is a place where many gurus have learned to conquer the mind."

Later in the day, I was outside, standing alone next to the well and looking up at the house I had built for Marpa. I was thinking of my labors and the many experiences I had had since I had come into the Nar Valley. I had the odd sensation that something was about to happen to me and that I might die in the process. I wasn't frightened by the prospect, knowing that at least Marpa would be with me. I didn't want to die yet. I wanted, first, to clean away the waste and destruction from my life, to make something worthwhile out of myself while in the physical life, but I also sensed that if I did die, I would discover little difference between life and death. If life was a dream, then death, it seemed, must also be a dream, a limbo between consciousness and unconsciousness. I wanted to live merely to realize the meaning of the dream, and then, if I had to give up my physical body in death, I wouldn't care.

"May I join you?" Nadar asked, coming up alongside me. She was wiping her hands on a kitchen cloth.

I held out my hand to her. "I was looking backward and forward in time," I said, looking toward the hill.

"There have been many changes – in you and the hill," Nadar said lightly.

I turned to face her. She was smiling warmly at me. I laughed at her joke and squeezed her hand. "There have indeed been many changes in the hill," I said. "Does your husband have any idea of what he will do with the house I have built him?"

"He has been talking about using it as an overnight sanctuary for weary travelers," Nadar said.

I was pleasantly surprised. "A wonderful Idea!" I said. "I had considered that the house, not having any purpose, would be torn down."

"No. Your guru feels that the mental impressions with which you formed the house may keep the transients transient. It will be what he calls the perfect guest house. He claims no one will want to stay too long in the place."

I did not know what to say and turned my head away, looking at the towering monument on the hill and then at Nadar again. She laughed, and I could not help but laugh with her. It was true. The house was monstrous, filled with the ghosts of my thoughts, as well as my blood, my sweat, and thousands of my tears.

"You are going to the Echo Cave tomorrow," Nadar said matter of factly.

I turned to her. "Yes," I answered uneasily, "but the guru didn't tell me how long I will be gone."

"It doesn't matter," Nadar said. "The length of time you are there doesn't matter. What matters is that you succeed in your intention."

I looked into the kindly face opposite me, considering that, as wife to the guru, she had probably experienced much herself. Nadar's eyes were filled with knowledge. "You have contemplated there?" I asked.

"Yes."

I was not surprised. I thought of the previous night and how, on Marpa's instructions, she had rescued me. She was probably a Lama herself.

She gazed up at me, as if she knew what I was thinking. "It was the guru who rescued you," she said. "I merely carried out his instruction to do so."

I hesitated. Nadar's tiny eyes sparkled in her round face. Although she was not a beautiful woman, there was a beauty about her. I felt sure that she would have rescued me even if Marpa had not.

"It was not Marpa, the man, who saved you," Nadar said, "but the guru in him. The guru saved you, alerting me to go to you." She hesitated, studying me, as if to see if I understood. "It is not an easy concept to grasp," she said, "but it will come in time."

*"Accidents do not exist.
...Accidents and misfortune are mere reflections
of a person's attention. The quality of one's
attention is the determining factor of the outcome."*

CHAPTER EIGHTEEN
ECHO CAVE

I stood next to Marpa in front of the large, oval opening to Echo Cave, the guru's giant hand resting affectionately upon my shoulder, while Thither engineered the movements of the yak carrying my provisions up the side of the mountain. The inside of the cave was plainly visible—an almost perfectly round room, large enough to stand or to lie down in. On the far wall was a fireplace. A thin shaft of light, cascading across a slim piece of black-burnt wood, indicated that the spot was well ventilated from above. On either side of the fireplace was a ledge. There was nothing on it.

"Come," Marpa said, motioning to me to follow him through the opening.

I stepped inside, suddenly surrounded by the cool air of the cave room. It was dry and yet I could smell the moisture that swelled beyond the thickness of rough rock. I tried to regulate a slow and even breath, but I found myself breathing deeper than normal, exploring what I could with my senses.

Thither led the yak into the room, calming it with a gentle pat as it shook itself in the unfamiliar environment. On a cue from Marpa, he unloaded it, carefully placing the supplies in a row along the ledge on either side of the fireplace. When he had finished, the guru thanked him and turned to me.

"All that you need is at hand," Marpa said, motioning to the supplies that Thither had left. "There is food, water, yak butter for tea, and fuel ... even a flint to begin your fires." He paused, looking deeply at me. "You are here to witness the attitudes that bind you," he said. "As you begin to recognize them, do not grow impatient with yourself. It is not possible to force spiritual unfoldment." He touched me in the center of my forehead, between and above the eyes. "Keep your attention here, at the seat of Consciousness. Think of this spot, in the center of your forehead, as a place where you and I can meet." He lowered his hand and gazed deeply into me. It was as though he had entered the sanctity of my inner being and was witnessing the pull of opposing forces within me. I did not speak, unsure that I could. "When you truly learn tolerance," Marpa said, "the resistant forces that separate you from realizing the nature of yourself will melt away, as naturally as the snow melts in the warmth of spring. Your existence will then be without resistance, and all things will fall into place, and the height of your dreams will be realized."

"How can I learn tolerance?" I asked uneasily.

"Patience is the seed of tolerance," the guru answered, "and patience is achieved by living in the present moment. Yesterday's memories are NOW. The dreams of tomorrow are forged NOW, in this moment. Do not allow your attention to wander back into the past and do not allow it to advance into the future. Live in the moment, keenly attuning your senses to the tiniest details of it."

I could think of nothing to say and remained silent, gazing into the guru's eyes, sensing the profound love he felt for me. I had never felt such love. It was not the love Zesay and I shared, nor was it the love that I felt with Thither, and yet this love was the sum total of it all. The love, which poured from Marpa's eyes into me was a limitless love. Through his gaze, I seemed to touch all eternity, the eternity beyond eternity and, for a split second, I was transported to this ALL NOTHINGNESS PLACE, becoming IT, becoming one with the guru, as well.

Marpa did not speak, but turned and started out of the cave to where Thither waited with the yak. As I watched him leave, I could feel the aloneness closing in about me, yet I made no effort to follow him.

Now outside, Marpa turned to face me. "Are you ready, Mila?" he asked, affectionately calling me by my pet name.

I swallowed, trying to ease the dryness that glued my mouth, and nodding, I finally spoke. "Yes, my guru, I am ready," I answered.

Marpa hesitated briefly, looking at me, then signaled to Thither, who disappeared from view for a moment and then returned, sliding a thick slab of rock across the opening and sealing me inside. The cave was suddenly dark, except for the minute stream of light above the fireplace.

I shivered in the sudden darkness, folding my arms about my chest, listening to the shuffle of movement outside. It was Marpa, Thither, and the yak beginning their descent down the mountain, leaving me sealed within the cave. I listened until I could no longer hear them, then turned and looked into the deep darkness.

After a moment, I stooped down before the fireplace, crumpled some filings of yak dung into a neat pile, and reached to the ledge for the flint, striking it against the rock and creating a spark next to the dry dung. The fire caught. In a moment, the dark cave began to glow with light and warmth. I added a few sticks to the blaze and then quickly busied myself, organizing the provisions that had been left me. There was a blanket and a yak fleece for a mattress. I looked about and chose a spot, spreading the fleece in front of the fire with the blanket folded on top of it. Next, I sorted the food. There was jerky and tsamba and root vegetables, butter for tea and water. There was also a lamp and a large container of yak oil. The lamp I left on the ledge next to the fireplace, and reaching for a burning stick, I lit it. This done, I extinguished the fire to conserve the fuel and sat down on the fleece to think out my situation.

Weird shapes danced across the rock walls in the dim light of the oil lamp. The air became suddenly cool again. I shivered. Marpa had not said how long I was to remain in confinement. I had been left provisions to last several weeks, perhaps even a month, if I carefully rationed them. I shivered again. A month in the earthy, cool confines of the cave was a much greater feat than the solitary life I had led on the hill while building Marpa's house. On the hill, I was in the open, free to come and go as I pleased. Now, confined in the cave, I was trapped.

Or was I?

Did Thither leave the opening ajar so that I could slip out?

I crossed to the huge slab of rock and leaned against it. It did not budge. Again, I leaned against it, this time my feet firmly planted on the ground, and I pushed with all my strength. The rock was unmoved and seemingly unmovable. I became frightened, feeling that I had been buried alive, but I quickly arrested the feeling, reminding myself that I was there for a purpose. Marpa had said that I was there to discover my attitudes.

A faint tinkling of bells sounded. I turned, looking about the still, rock chamber. Then, I heard them again. I tuned my ear to the rock but heard nothing. I called out to the stillness, listening to the thick sound of my voice coming back at me from within the cave. I began to think again, comparing solitude in the open with solitude in the cave but stopped suddenly, listening, realizing that when I compared one with the other that the sound of tinkling bells followed, and that they seemed to come from within myself, rather than from somewhere outside the cave. Did the bells have anything to do with what I was thinking? Were they an inner signal to alert me to pay attention to some important thought? Could it be that the bells followed some attitude that I was to recognize? Again, I listened, at first, hearing nothing. Then, focusing on the differences between freedom and confinement, and comparing my feelings about them, I heard the bells again. There was no doubt that they were coming from within myself and that they sounded to signal my attention.

Suddenly, it struck me. Marpa had said that my purpose in Echo Cave was to discover the nature of my attitudes, to recognize how my attitudes affected my vision of life. The fact that I was thinking of confinement and comparing it with whatever freedom I had known expressed attitudes that I had about confinement and freedom. It was the expression of these attitudes that caused the bells to sound. The bells were indeed signaling me. They were a form of the voice of silence, calling out to catch my attention.

I was fascinated by the idea, remembering other silent sounds and the forms they had taken, recalling the occasion of my initiation when I had heard a faint, thin, high-pitched sound. I recalled how the sound had seemingly changed from thin and faint, adding short abrupt pauses, like pebbles dropping into a pool of water. I wondered if Consciousness prompted audible orchestration in the visible world; if its purpose was to make us listen to the deeper meaning of things. The bells, in particular, seemed to signify the expression of an attitude binding a point of view. I was intrigued by the idea that there seemed to be inner ears as well as outer ears, and that the inner seemed to reflect the outer, that the outer was merely a denser version of the inner. It also occurred to me that there might be an inward/outward sight connection, as well. If that were the case, then there must be a whole and entirely invisible person to complement the visible.

I paused in thought, listening, hoping to hear something. It seemed that I heard nothing, but then I realized that in the nothing, the silence, there was sound. It was thin and remote, so high-pitched that it was barely audible. It was the sound that I had first become aware of at my initiation.

I was excited. I had not been in the cave more than a few hours and already I had made a major discovery. If only I could tell Marpa of it.

Thinking of the guru, I remembered that at the hermitage along the river I had literally made invisible contact with him while in meditation. Perhaps it was time to achieve that contact again.

Sitting erect, I folded my legs beneath me and drew in a long,deep breath and then slowly exhaled. Breathing deeply again, I closed my eyes. I thought of Marpa, imagining the details of his face and the powerful lines of his great body sitting opposite me, and when I had the image securely in mind, I gazed at the guru directly in the eyes.

Marpa winked at me.

Startled, I opened my eyes and looked about the cave. The same peculiar shapes danced weirdly on the rock walls above the lamp. Had I unknowingly slipped into sleep and had a dream that I had seen Marpa? I tried to calm the excitement that was growing in me.

Sitting erect, I took several more deep breaths and began to relax, closing my eyes. Again, I thought of Marpa. The image of the guru came more quickly this time. "Are you real?" I asked, questioning the vision.

Marpa did not speak, he smiled and comically rolled his eyes at me.

The realness of his image startled me, and I again opened my eyes.

The cave met my sight. I was still seated in the center of the fleece. The lamp still flickered, only now the deep scent of the cool air was thickened by the fumes of yak oil.

Excited, I closed my eyes and imaged Marpa before me again. "You are real?" I said to the master.

"But of course, I am real," Marpa answered, matter of factly. "Did you ever really doubt it?"

I didn't answer but looked around the room where I sat with the guru. It was Marpa's work chamber. The shelves and scrolls lined the walls about us. Marpa held a writing tablet on his lap. He had been writing something, scratching a message onto the dark surface of it.

"This black tablet is your cave," Marpa said. "It is black only because you believe it to be dark. In truth, it is only your consciousness that is dark." He paused, gazing at me. After a moment, he pointed to the writing he had done on the surface of the board. Because he had etched it onto a black tablet, the writing appeared as streaks of light on it. "See what I have written here," Marpa said, holding up the tablet for me to see.

I lowered my eyes to the tablet and read:

THE CAVE IS A SYMBOL OF YOUR INNER BEING
IT CAN BE FILLED WITH DARKNESS OR WITH LIGHT.

I looked up into the guru's quick eyes. "I don't understand," I said.

"What don't you understand?" Marpa asked, lowering the tablet to his lap.

I hesitated, inwardly arguing with the words the guru had etched on the tablet.

"Speak up," Marpa said. "What is it you do not understand?"

I glanced at the tablet and then looked directly at the guru again. "In their natural state, caves are dark," I answered finally.

Marpa nodded. "It is the way they appear to the outer eyes," he answered. "To the inner eyes of the awakened man, darkness does not exist."

"But a cave is still a dark place," I argued.

A faint smile formed on Marpa's lips, and he shook his head.

"There are many things that we are led to believe before we awaken to the truth. In the dream of life, we are bombarded with logic and rationalizations."

The guru's words reverberated in my thoughts. "In the dream of life," he had said. There was a part of me that knew that statement to be true. I recalled that since I had been in Nar, I had had many such awarenesses. Many times, I had felt myself on the edge of waking up, as though I had been asleep and dreaming my way through life. I had explored the idea that dreams were a series of images passing through the mind, visions in imagination; that memory, as well, was an image, only unlike a dream in that a memory was a series of images solidified. I had decided that dreams were the stuff of life—that sleep, daydreams, and experiences were filled with images of symbolic drama. But I had not considered what created the dream images.

I searched the guru's face in an effort to understand. "You are beginning to learn, Mila," he said smiling. "Life is a dream, but the dream has become so commonplace to many that they cannot see it. The only dream they recognize is the one in which their bodies rest in sleep. They do not realize that life is a result of our daydreams, that it is woven by the private fantasies of our imaginations. The life that we live in the world of touchable things is but a hardened symbol of our fantasies." Marpa paused, gazing at me with kindly eyes. "Tell me, Mila, which is real, being here with me now or being alone in the cave?"

I did not answer but sat looking at the guru, studying the upturned creases in his fleshy face. There was no doubt that he was sitting before me and, yet, how could I be sure.

The guru handed the tablet to me. The weight of it forced my arms to my lap. I looked up at Marpa. I wanted to believe that I was really with him.

"Which is real—the cave or the tablet?" Marpa asked.

He paused, waiting for me to answer but, uncertain, I remained silent. "A very great teacher has said that 'Life is nothing more than Consciousness meeting itself in the reflection of the outer world,'" Marpa said quietly, reverently. "Do you understand, Mila?"

Although I was touched by the familiar version of my name, I did not know what to answer.

"What I am telling you is that life is a dream, a reflected image, a stage on which Consciousness may perform." Marpa paused, studying the uncertain look on my face. "Life is a dream, Mila," he said again. Marpa held out his arms. "Life, or the dream, is created by the individual's mind. You already guessed it when you realized, while working on the hillside, that creation is a product of a succession of images passing through an individual's mind. Creation is one word. Life is another, and dream is another still. Yet all three—creation, life, and dream—mean the same thing. Reality is the effect of imagination. We awaken from life's dream when we realize what we are doing, how we are creating our personal worlds by the images passing through our minds and take control of them."

"Will the images then cease to exist?" I asked.

Marpa shook his great head. "No," he answered. "Since the images create life, we would cease to live without them, and we do not want to do that."

"Why not?" I asked. "Did you not say life was a dream? If that is the case, then why both?"

"A dream, yes," Marpa answered, "but the dream is important. Consciousness experiences through the dream. IT learns. IT has the opportunity to realize ITSELF and IT has the opportunity to realize the Void."

I hesitated a moment, wanting to ask about Consciousness and the Void, but instead, I said, "Then what is death?"

"It is a continuation of the dream in another form. In other words," Marpa said, "the dream continues on after death until that point where Consciousness recognizes ITSELF. It then no longer finds it necessary to dream." He stopped speaking and rose from his seat. He went to the window between the rows of shelves and looked out.

I understood what I had been told, and yet I did not understand. I watched the guru. He had his back to me as he gazed silently out the window. "Am I dreaming now?" I called out.

"Yes," Marpa answered softly without turning around. "You are dreaming, Mila."

An odd dream-like feeling settled over me, and I pinched myself, shifting the weight of the tablet from one hand to the other. There was pain, as well as the weight of the tablet, which seemed heavier now than before. If I was dreaming, it would seem that I should awaken at the signal of pain, yet life was filled with pain. Perhaps pain and joy were only illusions of the dream, of life.

Marpa was still standing before the window, looking out, when I asked, "What is it about imagination that creates the dream we call life?"

The guru answered without turning to face me. "It is the reason you are sealed in Echo Cave, Mila. Discover the reason, and you will discover your freedom."

I began to worry, when I recalled how I had deliberately decided to visit with Marpa even though I was enclosed in a cave.

Marpa suddenly turned from the window and looked at me. "Yes, you are getting to it, little Mila," he said quickly.

I was startled by the guru's acknowledgment of my thought and how the light from the window radiated his presence.

"You are not here in your physical body, although it may seem to be so," Marpa said. "You are here in your etheric body , in a setting produced by your mind. Mind dreams. Consciousness is the dreamer of dreams. Consciousness experiences through the dream, through whatever the mind consciousness allows it to experience." He paused, raising his hands and pressing the closed palms against his lips as if to silently pray. After a moment, he lowered them again. "Mila, do listen closely to what I am about to tell you." He paused again, waiting for my full attention. "You are in the cave, and yet you are here at the same time. Your physical body is in the cave. Your Consciousness is here with me. The tablet you have in your hands is real, and the fact that you are holding it is real." Marpa paused, taking a step closer. "But if someone were to walk into this room right now, they would see only the tablet resting on the cushion. You would not be seen at all." He paused again, studying the curious expression on my face. "There is much you will have to figure out for yourself," Marpa said, "but that will take time. You have been given that time. Use it wisely. Practice the movement of Consciousness. Do this by leaving your body in quiet repose within the safety of the cave and spend as much time as you can out of it. Gradually, you will notice that as you imagine someone in your mind, you will be with that person."

"BEWARE!" Marpa warned, gazing deeply into my eyes before continuing. "Gently bless those who have shared in the composition of your life without intruding on their privacy. Love a person always in a detached way, your emotions intact, so that the person feels freedom in your presence, not anxiety. When you tire of others or feel uneasy, think of me, and you will be with me. I am always with you, guiding you, protecting you, loving you. Someday, it will come to pass that your mind will be still. You will think of nothing, imagine no one, not even me. That day you will begin the experience of freedom, true freedom. Consciousness will no longer require dreams to experience ITSELF in life. You will come and go in the high planes of consciousness, even while you maintain a physical body here in the lower world. It is a state liberated men call the golden dream. When this happens, Mila, you will leave the cave."

As I sat, gazing up at the guru, I felt a wave of love coming from him to me, and in that wave, I again heard the faint, high-pitched music within myself. I began to sense again the dream of being with the guru and the reality of it. The sensing was not in the touch, smell, or sight of the experience, although I could draw them to mind, but rather, in my vision or perception of being there. I recalled that the guru had explained how the mind dreams and how Consciousness perceives the dream, and for an instant, I knew, truly knew, the meaning of the words.

Marpa smiled and nodded. He had heard my inner voice. "You are beginning to awaken, Mila," he said in a gentle voice. "Take it slowly. There is no rush. Once the process has begun, it weaves its way into a person's consciousness. You have to work at it, of course, constantly probing with diffused inner vision. And, even after you believe you understand everything, the process continues. There is always more. It is never over, not ever. An awakened person is always involved in the subtle interplay of the self and emptiness."

Overwhelmed by the guru's love, my eyes flooded with tears, and I lowered them, resting my gaze on the tablet Marpa had given me. Again, I read:

THE CAVE IS A SYMBOL OF YOUR INNER BEING.
IT CAN BE FILLED WITH DARKNESS OR WITH LIGHT.

I understood. When I raised my eyes to Marpa again, instead of seeing the guru, I found myself sitting teary-eyed and alone in the cave. After a time, I went to the rock wall and, over the ledge, I used the flint to scratch the words upon it that had been written on the tablet.

THE CAVE IS A SYMBOL OF YOUR INNER BEING
IT CAN BE FILLED WITH
DARKNESS OR WITH LIGHT

CHAPTER NINETEEN
BANISHING PHANTOMS

When I awoke, my lamp had gone out and the cave was dark and cold. I shivered and drew the blanket up close about my chin, recalling dream-like images of Marpa and a message he had given me. I remembered that I had scratched the words on the cave wall. Rising to a sitting position, I reached to the ledge and slid my hand along it, finally locating the piece of flint and the lamp that was next to it. I then struck the flint against the rock wall. Sparks flew and quickly dissipated. After a few tries, a spark caught the wick, and the dark cave suddenly glowed with light. In front of me on the wall were the words: THE CAVE IS A SYMBOL OF YOUR INNER BEING. IT CAN BE FILLED WITH DARKNESS OR WITH LIGHT.

Amazed, I folded my legs beneath me and sat staring at the wall, contemplating the memory of my meeting with Marpa and the meaning of what I had written on the wall. Was the cave truly a symbol of my inner being? Was my physical body locked within the cave merely to perceive the symbol? To grasp its significance?

What did it mean?

Was my presence there purely symbolic, or was it more than my inner being that had a choice between darkness and light? The answer came to me, expanding the parameters of mind. It seemed that the true answer connected the inner being with the outer being; that life within the cave, as well as life within the imagination, could be filled with light; that the lamp, which now illuminated the cave, was unnecessary. The idea seemed absurd, and yet, Marpa had said that life was a dream and that we choose not only the environment and scenery of the dream, but all that transpires within the dream, as well. I understood, and yet I did not understand. If, in truth, life was a dream, then why would I dream such tedious and oftentimes hideous dreams? Did I choose the wretched childhood that followed my father's death? Did I choose the experience of the black magician's monastery? Or revenge? If that were the case, however, I had chosen some fine dreams, as well ... befriending Thither, loving Zesay, initiation with Marpa.

The writing on the wall danced in the flickering light. It was both legible and illegible, sometimes distinct and at other times entirely invisible. I thought of all that had happened to me since my arrival in Nar and how it had all seemed both real and unreal. Was the reality, or lack of it, a dream of my choice? I gazed about the cave. Here I was in an unbelievable situation. I had allowed myself to be entombed inside a rock room, had agreed to remain until I discovered the nature of my attitudes and how they bind me. Suppose I never discovered it?

The lamp sputtered and sent off a shower of sparks and then flickered a few times. Was it attitude that made the choice of which dreams one would live?

Concentrating deeply, I raised my hands to my mouth and covered it, looked over my fingertips to the scribbling I had done on the cave wall, and considered what it was that Marpa wanted me to learn. Gradually, it dawned on me what an attitude was ... a way of acting or feeling. An attitude was formed by clinging to a feeling. Attitude was belief, and belief controlled our view of life. I held my breath, barely breathing, realizing that every time I had become fixed in my attitudes, my attention became locked, riveted on a particular point of view, and that that viewpoint was the vantage point from which I lived life. My viewpoint dictated what I saw, heard, and experienced in the environment. I was wherever I placed my attention, drawing events to me and pushing them away. It struck me that when I placed my attention on someone or something, the feeling part of me formed attitudes, naturally selecting the cycle that I then lived.

The lamp sputtered again as I strained to study the words I had scratched onto the wall. THE CAVE IS THE SYMBOL OF YOUR INNER BEING. IT CAN BE FILLED WITH DARKNESS OR WITH LIGHT.

Stunned by the realization, I closed my eyes. For a time, I was unthinking and unfeeling, seeing nothing within my own quiet inner world except light, brilliant, intense light, until gradually, I saw that in front of my inner vision was a pale-blue, transparent image of Marpa. Although I could not see his eyes, I knew the guru was gazing at me. "Thank you," I called lovingly from within the silent recesses of my heart. There was a pause, during which the pale-blue image of the guru expanded, reaching out to me. A silent wave of love rushed back to me, filling me, overflowing from me back toward the faint image of the guru. Again, the wave of love was returned. I gratefully accepted it, allowing it to flow freely through me to the guru and back again, over and over, joining us, and with it came the melodies of our love. The music was so beautiful, both alluring and eluding, that I could not describe it. Slowly, the vision faded, and I opened my eyes again.

I sat motionless, trying to adjust to the semi-darkness of the cave. The light from the yak-oil lamp, which had once seemed to brighten the place, now appeared grey and dingy. The thick smell of the yak fat thinned into oil was disturbing to me and, without thinking, I leaned forward and blew it out. The cave immediately brightened again. Although the yak-oil lamp had been extinguished, the cave was clearly lit with a brilliant white light. Looking about, I rose to my feet, aware that the damp chill had been replaced by warmth. I touched the wall and again read what I had written there. THE CAVE IS A SYMBOL OF YOUR INNER BEING. IT CAN BE FILLED WITH DARKNESS OR WITH LIGHT.

I walked in circles around the round cave, marveling at the splendor of my discovery, aware of a faint music and the sweet scent of roses that filled the chamber. The memory of the guru's love lingered and, for a time, I relaxed in the joy that had sprung in my heart.

The light remained constant as I considered the endless possibilities of my discovery. If a mental image of the guru could produce light and warmth, what would happen if another type of mental image formed?

Realizing that I was in the cave to experience and learn from the depths of my being, I decided to experiment. I seated myself on the fleece, and with eyes closed, I began to contemplate an image of myself, sitting beside a clear, blue river. The image came slowly, but gradually, I did see the river. It was surrounded by rhododendrons and evergreens and there was a small clearing in which I was sitting next to the water. It was a pleasant sight, and I felt at home in it. I touched the ground next to me and then slipped my hand into the cool water just to be sure it was real. I thought of Zesay and of the river where we had met, where she had disappeared, leaving me and, almost expecting to see her, I turned my head and gazed downstream. There, on a rope footbridge, I recognized the graceful movements of the young woman making the crossing; when she reached the end, she paused and turned toward me.

My breath caught as I rose to my feet. For a moment, I was unable to move, and then I ran to her and she to me, and I caught her in my arms.

"Mila! Oh, Mila!" she cried, wrapping her arms about me. "You have done it. You have conquered the little self."

I hesitated, enraptured by the warmth of her body next to mine, holding her for as long as she yielded, and then, aware of a slight resistance, I released her and gazed lovingly into her eyes.

Zesay smiled. "I am so happy to see you, Mila," she said.

I gazed at her for a long while, enraptured by the feeling of her presence and the glow of beauty that radiated from her face. "Did you have to leave me that day at the hermitage?" I asked, finally.

Her eyes dimmed and a wrinkle furrowed her brow. "I thought you understood, Mila," she said, in a disturbed voice. "I was never there in my physical body. I had to return to it, Mila, to fulfill my responsibilities within the body form."

Although I was beginning to understand, knowing that we were not meeting in our physical bodies, I was not yet comfortable with the concept. "Will you stay with me now?" I asked, wishing that I had said nothing.

"Mila," she said in a quiet, patient voice, "do you understand that we are not here in our physical bodies?"

I nodded, touching the fingers of my right hand to her lips. I knew it, but I also knew that Zesay was real, that her presence was with me. I could smell the sweet scent of her flesh near me.

"It depends," she said, smiling. "It depends on how long the dream lasts."

"Let's make it last," I said.

"It may not be that easy," she said. "But now that you know the secret, we can have many such meetings."

I became concerned that she might suddenly disappear and I would not remember how to reach her again.

"Some dreams are sleeping dreams; some dreams are day dreams or contemplations, such as this one; and some dreams are waking dreams, which are physical experiences. All of life is a dream," she said finally and, sensing my wonderment, she reached for my hand and held it between hers. She squeezed it and then held it to her face, rubbing my large hand against her soft cheek. "I love you, Mila," she said softly.

I was thinking about what she had said and was too astounded to answer. It was what Marpa had been telling me; only, until now, I could not grasp the reality of it. Marpa had explained the dream, and yet, the reality of dreaming, that I was dreaming still eluded me. I recalled the weight of the writing tablet on my lap, an experience that was not physical, but, like this one with Zesay, was lived in subtler form. "Zesay, what is a dream?" I asked, filled with wonder.

She squeezed my hand and lowered it from her face, holding it tightly at her side, touching the folds of her skirt. "A dream is a succession of images passing through the mind," she answered. "Reality is the effect of these images." She hesitated, studying me. "Most people," she said again, "get so wrapped up in the dream of living that they don't realize that they are merely acting out a wishful experience."

I stared at her for a long while, wondering how she knew such things and yet sensing that what she said was true. It was as if lightening were striking at various centers within me. "How do you know these things?" I asked.

Zesay turned and looked dreamily down river and then turned to face me again. "When you left our village to avenge your family, I thought my life was over," she said sorrowfully. "I became sick and weak in my grieving for you. For weeks, I barely ate, and as time went by, I grew pale and ill." She hesitated, looking away briefly before she continued. "And then the good Lama Kataka came to me in a sleeping dream one night and told me that if I wanted to see you again, I could do so. He told me that if I would seek instruction from him again, he would teach me the way. When I awoke, I knew the dream to be no ordinary dream. It was not symbolic or muddled with my previous daily affairs. I recognized it as an offer and a promise from the Lama, and I very quickly went for instruction again."

"And did he remember your dream, as well?" I asked.

"He didn't say, but then he was not surprised to see me either," Zesay answered. "Since then, he has taught me to come and go from my body at will."

"And did you learn in a cave, as well?" I asked.

Zesay shook her head. "No, Mila, I did not learn in a cave, nor have I lived in one."

"Where is it you live?" I asked quickly.

Zesay was slow in answering. "I live here in your dream," she said. "My physical body is in a nunnery a great distance from here. I do work at a loom, in a place much like where we met. Perhaps that is why you were drawn to me so quickly at the hermitage."

I searched her face, noting that she was even more beautiful than I remembered her, and I sensed that, although I could be with her almost anytime, I would never again meet her person in physical form.

"It doesn't really matter," she said, as if listening to my thoughts. "You have a greater mission now."

"I have no mission, Zesay," I said, "except to save myself from the damnation of my deeds."

She shook her head slowly from side to side. "Your deeds have provided the springboard for what is to come," Zesay said, gazing at me. "Your future is a glorious one."

I searched her beautiful face for meaning. I wanted to kiss her to feel the softness of her cheeks against my rough skin, and to whisper the glorious murmuring of my heart into her ears, but instead, I merely gazed at her, loving her with my eyes.

"Tell me about the cave in which you live," Zesay said.

The surprise of her request jolted me. My body twitched, and suddenly, prompted by a popping sound in my ears, I envisioned the cave and opened my eyes. My gaze was met by the rough rock wall. Zesay was gone. I was alone, lonely and confused. As I sat staring in the empty space, feeling the great loss of my beloved, the light in the cave began to fade, growing dimmer and dimmer until finally, I went to the lamp and lit it. The thick, musty smell of the burning yak oil met my nostrils but the stench comforted me. There was a realness to the smell of yak oil that seemed logical and right, unlike the unnatural light that had reflected the guru's presence. In fact, part of me doubted the experience had happened at all. I decided that both Marpa's and Zesay's appearances had occurred at a time when I had fallen asleep and were mere dreams. I convinced myself that there was no reality to dreams at all, that they were merely dreams.

In the days that followed, I argued within myself, recalling Marpa and Zesay and how both had said that life was composed of various states of the dream experience. I compared the words of one with those of the other, mentally searching for discrepancies, but could find none. Although at various times I had considered life to be dream-like, the idea, as presented by Marpa and Zesay, that all life was a dream seemed both absurd and shocking to me. And for some reason, which I couldn't explain to myself, I felt angry.

As the dayless hours slipped by, I became more and more morose. Would no one ever come to let me out of the place? Frequently, I went to the slab of rock, which covered the opening, and pounded on it with my fists, calling out in hope that someone would hear. The rock was solid and did not move, and I knew that its thickness made it soundproof. There was no response.

Oftentimes, I tried to calm myself with memories of my childhood before my father's death, but I could not ignore the icy air that rose from the dirt floor penetrating the yak fleece on which I sat.

Time seemed endless.

Gradually, my anger turned to fear. Suppose no one would come to release me from the cave? Was I to die such a wretched death as payment for my deeds? Would I go mad? Was I already going mad?

Then one day, the lamp went dark and I could not relight it. I hurried on my knees, scratching the flint on the rock, but the sparks did not ignite the lamp. It finally occurred to me that the oil was gone. There was nothing I could do.

The damp-darkness seemed to close in about me. I reached to the ledge and stuffed the last of the food into my mouth, remembering how I had eaten and drunk on impulse, certain that I would be rescued by Marpa or Thither when they believed that I had been sealed in long enough, or when I realized that my confinement was a dream, a very nasty dream, and I awoke from it. But no one had come and I did not awaken.

I was afraid.

Sinking back down to the fleece, I pulled the blanket up close about my neck. The darkness was so dark that I could see nothing, just black emptiness. It was as if my body no longer existed, as though I was lost in a terrible void. I lowered my face into the folds of the blanket to warm the air I was breathing. I thought of my mother. When I was a child, before my father's death, she warmed me, nestled next to her bosom. Imagining myself safe and detached, I tried to see my terrible reality as a dream, that Marpa and perhaps Zesay were trying to trick me into believing the cave was real. One thing puzzled me above all else. I had no idea if I was awake or asleep or even if I was dead, living an afterlife of doom as Narquin had suggested that I would.

The idea struck me oddly. Perhaps all of my memories – leaving my family, Zesay, my evil deeds, building Marpa's hilltop houses, and initiation – were all part of a dream, unreal, a nasty trick of the senses.

"Milarepa, when will you learn?" A voice shouted in the darkness.

Knowing that I was alone in the cave, I was certain that the voice was an illusion and did not try to answer back.

"No one is ever alone in the darkness," the voice said again. "Darkness is a void of consciousness, a hiding place for ignorant ideas, and it is filled with phantoms, which is why you are in it."

I listened to the voice and identified it as Narquin's. Terrified, I huddled deeper into my blanket, hiding myself from the darkness.

"Why are you putting yourself through all of this?" Narquin asked.

Too terrified to speak, I could not answer. Again, I tried to think of my early childhood, of my mother when she was loving, of my father, of playing with my sister Peta and of how we would cuddle in our mother's and father's arms. Remembering seemed to work for a moment, and I began to relax.

"A good trick of the imagination," Narquin said, interrupting my fantasy, "but I am the height of your imagination at this moment. You must therefore pay attention to me, not to your childhood. Your childhood is past. I am now. Listen to me and heed my words." There was a long pause in the thick darkness. I shivered, then heard Narquin speak again. "I am a part of your imagination," Narquin said, "and your imagination is a part of you. There is little else to life." He paused briefly. I could feel his icy eyes reaching out to me from the darkness. "Do you think that the great Lama Yungtun-Trogyal could have trained you to call upon the elements to destroy a village if you had not had a strong imagination to draw the power? A weak imagination draws little power from life. A strong imagination draws great power."

"Then it is true that imagination is the power of life," I said, my voice sounding as if I were speaking from a great distance away. "It is the power of the dream."

"It is definitely the power of the dream," Narquin answered.

"If that is true," I said more boldly, "then how did you get here? I did not imagine you into this cave."

"I am part of your imagination, not all of it," Narquin said, his voice vibrating the darkness. "I am an unconscious part of your imagination, that part of you that clings to the walls of your mind. You are never without me because I have become a part of you. So, you see, it is not necessary for you to imagine me at all. I am here, waiting in the darkness to awaken in your moments of fear and confusion."

I listened without answering, remembering that I had held a fascination for Narquin, even admired him as the closest disciple to the black magician.

"Would you care to know who I really am?" Narquin asked.

I hesitated, uncertain if I should ask?

"Well?" Narquin prodded.

"Yes, who are you really?" I asked.

Specks of red light began to dance before me and, as though watching me watch was amusing, Narquin began to laugh. His laughter rose higher in pitch and lowered again, and each time it rose, I noticed that the speckles of red light multiplied, filling a certain section of the cave. I noticed that the ruby lights were like a series of dots, outlining a form. My skin prickled. The form, which I believed to be Narquin, was actually that of the Lama Yungtun-Trogyal. I was suddenly too terrified to breathe. My breath caught as I struggled for air. Was the Lama Yungtun-Trogyal actually Narquin?

"Narquin is a product of my imagination," the Lama answered, as if hearing my thought. "I created Narquin as a teaching tool, a handsome prototype of the negative expression. Narquin serves as a lure to assist me in communicating with the likes of you and others who could not otherwise withstand my actual vibration."

Memories of meeting the Lama came quickly to mind. At times, he had approached me gently, or so it had seemed. I also recalled the night in the contemplation hall when the Lama had ripped my heart from me.

"It was in that moment that you became my disciple," the sorcerer said. "When I took your heart, you were granted initiation and, in exchange, you became my property."

"Is this meeting with you a dream?" I asked, boldly.

"Yes," the Lama answered. "It is a dream. Our union has created it."

"I don't wish to dream of the negative forces any longer," I answered.

The Lama laughed, his cold eyes glaring at me. "No dream can exist without the involvement of negative imagination," the Lama said, making a short, clicking sound with his teeth. "Unless, of course, you know how," he added.

"What do you mean?" I asked.

"Will you come with me if I tell you?" the Lama asked, only it wasn't the Lama any longer but Narquin.

I felt suddenly inspired, as if I were inching my way to the final piece of the grand puzzle of life. I knew that to agree to go with Narquin meant instant death, both physical and spiritual. I also knew that, in order to survive, I had to know the answer. If only I could discover it on my own.

I drew in a deep breath. The cool air filled me, clearing my head. Marpa had put me here to discover my attitudes so that I would no longer be bound by anything. I did not wish to gain the knowledge only to succumb to Narquin's will, and yet, I knew that my despair had drawn Narquin to me. In the silence, it gradually struck me. If all of life was a dream and that dream was controlled by the imagination, I did not have to allow it to be controlled by the negative imagination. The negative imagination took hold when one was blind to options. It was one's attitudes that dictated the outcome. A negative attitude was an inner conflict, an imbalance in the personal power of the individual. In my unwillingness to recognize what I myself had brought to pass, my meetings with Marpa and Zesay, I had become frightened and intimidated by the negative side of my nature. Narquin was a prominent figure in that part of me.

I closed my eyes and thought of Marpa, drawing an image of the guru in my imagination. As my vision of him strengthened and he became visible, the signs of his presence also increased: a brilliant pale-blue light accompanied by the scent of roses and a feeling of well-being. I knew that the black magician had gone, and as I opened my eyes, I saw that the cave was once again filled with light. The darkness had gone. Directly in front of me on the cave wall was the message I had scratched: THE CAVE IS A SYMBOL OF YOUR INNER BEING. IT CAN BE FILLED WITH DARKNESS OR WITH LIGHT. The guru was sitting cross-legged in front of it, opposite me.

"How long have you been here in this cave?" Marpa asked casually.

Before, it was I who had, by some trick of the imagination, visited the guru, but now, it was the guru who visited me. He was actually here in the cave with me. I was surprised and hesitated, aware that he had asked me a question. "I don't know," I answered, uncertain. "A few days, perhaps."

"Or a few weeks," Marpa said seriously.

I hesitated again. If I had been in the cave a few weeks, then it was also likely that I had been unconscious most of the time.

"That's right, you have been unconscious," Marpa said, responding to my thoughts. "That is, your lack of awareness of time and its passage has made it seem so. Tell me, did you even once feel that you had been here too long, that you could bear the cave no longer?"

"Yes," I answered, nodding.

"At that moment, you were conscious of time. Your imagination was squeezed into feeling and imagining the NOW, and it didn't like it. You could have visited me and felt relief from the cave," Marpa said. He hesitated, staring deeply into me. "Do you know why you did not seek relief?"

"Because, at times, I forgot how," I answered stupidly.

"You forgot how, or you rejected the way out?" Marpa asked.

I shifted my weight uncomfortably. "I would never have rejected the way, my guru," I said.

"Then why didn't you come?" Marpa asked.

"Because I forgot the method of doing so," I answered.

Marpa raised his hand and brought it down heavily, striking me on the leg.

I grimaced at the pain of the guru's blow and stared at him in astonishment. The guru had never before struck me.

"Listen carefully, Milarepa," Marpa said, speaking slowly. "FORGOT is a word that indicates a cluttered mind. The guru never forgets. The guru is always aware. Memory is nothing more than awareness of awareness. It is the free flow of what has been and how it relates to what is, which relates to what will be." He paused, as if listening to the questions forming in my mind, then continued. "If a person is injured and loses memory, it is because his mind is jarred into confusion. The real question is, what caused the injury?"

I hesitated, waiting to see if the guru would continue. My leg still smarted from the blow.

"What caused the injury? Marpa asked again.

I answered that the cause could have been an accident, or that the injury could have been caused by a blow from another person.

"You have already learned that there is no such thing as an accident," Marpa said. "Accidents are a product of one's lack of attention to the moment, and very often, the attention is focused on something negative." He paused. "Why did I strike you?" Marpa asked.

"Because I was making excuses," I answered.

Marpa drew in a deep breath and exhaled slowly. He smiled. "Yes, Mila, because you were making excuses for yourself. At least, you strive for honesty." He reached over and rubbed my leg, and then sat up straight again. The pain had disappeared at the guru's touch.

I lowered my eyes and then raised them again. "You are saying that I have the capacity to control the outcome of my own life," I said.

Marpa nodded, his lips pursed thoughtfully. "Mila, what controls one's life? In particular, what controls your life?"

"I do," I answered.

"Who is I?" Marpa asked.

I hesitated thoughtfully, recalling the realization that I had had prior to the guru's appearance. "My imaginative faculty controls my life," I answered.

Marpa gestured with outstretched palms and then brought them together in praying fashion in front of his lips. "Yes, Mila," he said gently, "it is imagination that controls your life." He folded his hands, lowered them to his chest, and bowed his head. After a long moment, he raised his head again and looked deeply into my eyes. "Mila," he continued in a gentle voice, "what controls your imagination?"

I was held by the guru's gaze, mesmerized by it. I had a feeling of oneness, as well as separateness, as though the guru and I were one, joined, and yet individuals, that we had merged and yet we were separate. I had a distinct feeling of lightness, as though, if I wished, I could rise out of my body and fly.

"What answer comes to you, Mila?" The guru asked.

"Consciousness," I answered. My voice sounded as though it was coming from afar.

"And how does Consciousness perceive the imagination?" Marpa asked.

Again, I hesitated. It was as if suddenly NOTHING and EVERYTHING meant the same thing. "It sees nothing and yet it is witness to everything," I answered finally.

"And the thing IT is witnessing is what?" the guru prodded.

"Images," I answered, "images from the imagination."

"How do those images affect your life?" Marpa asked.

I closed my eyes and patiently watched as the images of my imagination passed across the screen of my mind. At times, I saw myself building Marpa's house. At other times, I saw the boy Jimilu leaning over his addicted mother as she lay on the ground at the back of their stall in the marketplace. I also saw Zesay and felt the touch of her hand. Casually watching these images, it occurred to me that each image created a feeling in me. I told the guru about the discovery.

"What do the feelings create?" Marpa asked, prodding again.

I again watched the images passing though my mind. As I felt the touch of Zesay's hand, I noticed that in addition to feeling love and warmth, I also felt possession, and the feeling struck sharp opinions in me, as though she was my property, that I owned her. I saw, too, that my imagery toward Jimilu and his mother had made me feel sorrow and pity, and those feelings, too, struck opinions in me. It was my opinion that the woman needed help; that the boy should not be left with her; that Thither was acting pompously about the situation, and so on. Suddenly, it struck me that the opinions I was expressing came from attitudes I had developed in life and that these attitudes were directly related to the images. The attitudes sprang from the images, from the imagination.

"Attitudes are controlled by imagination," the guru said suddenly, responding to my thoughts. "They are the direct results of where we have allowed our attention to roam and the aberrations and facsimiles we have collected during those adventures. It is a condition of mind control, of an individual's mind, collecting bits and pieces of information here and there, and permitting these bits and pieces to control one's view of life. As you can see, they can be very limiting."

"But what is there to do about it?" I asked.

The guru gazed at me seriously. "You must take control of the imagination," he answered.

"But you said that the imagination is controlled by mind," I argued.

"And you, Mila, suggested that it was Consciousness who inspired imagination," Marpa added. "You indicated to me that, once released from the conditions of mind, you would be free."

"But freedom has its limitations," I argued again.

"Does it?" Marpa asked.

"Yes," I said, definitely. "It does have its limitations. This cave for instance."

"What about it?"

"You and Thither sealed me in the cave. I cannot leave until the seal is broken," I said.

"THEN SEE IT THAT WAY!" the guru shouted.

The blow of the guru's words struck me in an awful way. I was shocked and sprang to my feet, suddenly aware that I was standing alone beneath a clear, blue sky. The light was soft but exceedingly bright. Marpa was gone, and I was standing alone outside the entrance to the cave, staring at the huge slab of rock that sealed it.

EPILOGUE

Rechung lowered the last tablet from which he had been reading, placed it on the floor on top of the others, then looked up at those gathered before him. No one moved or spoke and, in the silence of the great cave, the hush was extraordinary. The faces of young and old stared up at him, as though they were in contemplative shock, waiting for something that would release the tension of the story ending so abruptly.

A long moment passed. The feeling of expectancy turned into calm, accompanied by the soft, haunting hum, like the blowing of a trumpet in the distance. The calm filled Rechung as he listened and, certain that he recognized the sound, he raised his head. Before him on the platform was a glow of golden light. The scent of roses filled the air. Gazing lovingly into the light, he witnessed the form of the Vi-Guru unfolding as a blossom unfolds in a ray of sunlight, appearing next to him. In one smooth, even motion, the Jetsun was suddenly sitting next to Rechung.

"Thank you, my son," Milarepa said lovingly. Then he turned to gaze at those who had gathered to hear his story. A low murmur went through the crowd. To them, the Vi-Guru appeared at the precise moment he turned his gaze upon them.

Milarepa smiled, waiting for the surprise of those gathered to settle down, then he spoke. "There are those of you who believe that a more proper ending should be given to my story," he said. "I ask that you now speak up and voice the questions unsettling you."

There was a long pause in which everyone seemed to be too astounded to respond. Then at last, a woman called out. "Venerable Guru, your story is missing details that I would like to know." She hesitated, then at a nod from the Jetsun, continued. "You spoke of your sister Peta traveling to Katmandu to find livelihood, but never mentioned what became of her."

Milarepa answered. "Peta established a useful life as a servant for a time. She later married a kindly man in that city, and together, they raised three children, two boys and a girl, who came to them in need of a home." The Vi-Guru paused, gazing at the woman who had asked the question, and as though anticipating her next question, he added, "Zesay remains in the nunnery. She has never married."

The woman who had asked the question nodded appreciatively and spoke again. "Will the Jetsun also tell us what finally happened to his evil aunt and uncle?"

Milarepa closed his eyes and opened them again, as if the action drew forth memory. "There was a time when I was living in caves along the ridge of the mountains outside Nyang. I was naked and had been sustaining myself on pine needles for such a long period of time that my body fluids, when expelled, were green, and I knew that my health was in danger, and so I decided that I would seek alms among the cliff dwellers." He paused thoughtfully. "The first house that I came to was occupied by my aunt. When she opened the door and saw me, she believed I was a ghost and, in a frightened voice, begged my forgiveness. I told her that I had already forgiven her, but since fate had drawn us together again, I wished her forgiveness, as well."

"My aunt, suddenly aware that I had not come to punish her further for her mistreatment of my family, became irate and began screaming obscenities at me. She told me that I had made her and her husband suffer, and that her daughter had gone mad following the loss of her home and child, and that her daughter's husband had become an invalid. I was greatly ashamed as I listened to her story but realized that each also shared in the responsibility for his or her circumstances. My aunt then told me that they had moved to that place, high in the mountains, to ensure peace and quiet for the remainder of their lives."

"I told her that I had no wish to disturb them, but that I had been meditating in a cave for some time without food and stopped at her house for alms, not knowing that it was she who would receive me. My aunt then threw a piece of household cloth at me and told me to cover my nakedness. Then she gave me tsamba and meat and asked that I leave and not return. I accepted the gifts she had given me and left as she had requested, never to see them again."

A long, thoughtful silence followed the conclusion of the Jetsun's story. Finally, one man in the center of the gathering rose to his feet. He stood quietly for a moment before speaking. "My Guru, I wish to know what happened to you after you left Echo Cave."

A soft murmur went through the gathering, and then there was absolute stillness. All eyes were on the Jetsun, waiting for his answer.

"I filled my life with episodes that would teach me what I needed to learn," Milarepa said, his soft eyes twinkled in his round face. "Now and then, I returned to my guru Marpa's house, but mostly, I roamed the mountains, where I lived in caves, fasting and contemplating the ever-unfolding center of emptiness. I gradually unraveled the tapestry of my karma, and I learned the secrets of time and space. I also learned that by keeping my personal vibrations imperceptible, I could become invisible and could therefore come and go, being seen or unseen as I chose it. I also learned to transmute my vibrations into various forms. In the winter, I often assumed the form of a snow leopard as a tranquil means of adapting to the harsh climate of the mountains. I learned levitation, not of spirit alone, but of body and spirit. And all these things I learned through an increasing awareness of one simple rule." Milarepa paused and turning to Rechung, indicated with a motion of his hand that he should write his next words down.

The Vi-Guru slowly turned his head, gazing into the upturned faces before him. After a moment, he continued. "The rule I wish to give you is a life-long lesson, which you will experience on endless levels. It is this and nothing more: TRUST AND DISCIPLINE THE ATTENTION."

Milarepa rose to his feet and smiled. "The eventual path of the true disciple is the golden dream, where inwardly and outwardly, the silence sings the same song and you are aware, without commenting to yourself." He then turned to Rechung and placed a hand on his shoulder. "This is my true son, the son of my heart. He is known to you as Rechung, but the name I met him by is Jimilu." Milarepa was silent again, gazing, first, at those seated about him and then at Rechung. Tears streamed down Rechung's face as a circle of golden light suddenly enfolded Milarepa. The light was so bright that the Vi-Guru's form seemed to merge with it, becoming the golden light itself, until finally, he disappeared.

*"The golden dream happens in silence.
Its true name is love."*

BOOKS BY WISDOM MASTER MATICINTIN
available from Dharmavidya Publishing

The Book of Creation: Arising of Existence (2015)

The Lit Passageway (2014)

CHOD: Cutting Through Obstacles (2014)

The Memory Grid Between Life and Death (2011)

The Heart Sutra (2008)
(Decipher the priceless wisdom of one of Buddhism's shortest and most important sutras through a fresh, poetic rendering and its profound commentary.)

Logics from the Third Eye: Timeless Daily Wisdom (2007)

Secrets of the Golden Spiral: Handbook for Enlightenment (2006)

Come Dance with Me: A book of inspirational HÜMÜH Buddhist stories that provide spiritual realizations (2006)

Life Around Us (1996)
(An illustrated book for children of all ages with sing-along audio CD)

Writing as a Tool for Self-Discovery (1982)

Awakening Stone (1982)

Other Books from Dharmavidya Publishing:

Walking with the Wind by Terry Daniels (2020)

HÜMÜH Cooking - Our Most Delicious Vegetarian Recipes from Sky-cliffe HÜMÜH Buddhist Monastery (2018)

Initiation: Autobiography of a Shaman-Buddhist Apprentice by Sharon Shier (2005)

To order
Call: **1-800-336-6015**
Email: DharmavidyaPublishing@HUMUH.org
Website: www.humuh.org/humuh-store/books/

www.HUMUH.org

✔ *Check Here*

☐ **Yes,** I would like to receive information about becoming an Initiate of HÜMÜH.

☐ **Yes,** I would like to receive, *free of charge*, the *Daily Wisdom Teaching* by email.

Please Print Clearly or Call 1-800-336-6015

Name: _____

Address: _____

City & State/Province: _____

Zip/Postal Code: _____

Country: _____

E-mail: _____

You may also email your information to office@HUMUH.org.

✔ *Check Here*

☐ **Yes,** I would like to receive information about becoming an Initiate of HÜMÜH.

☐ **Yes,** I would like to receive, *free of charge*, the *Daily Wisdom Teaching* by email.

Please Print Clearly or Call 1-800-336-6015

Name: _____

Address: _____

City & State/Province: _____

Zip/Postal Code: _____

Country: _____

E-mail: _____

You may also email your information to office@HUMUH.org.

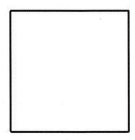

HÜMÜH™
Clear-Mind Buddhism
Transcendental Awareness Institute
P.O. Box 2700
Oroville, WA 98844

USA

HÜMÜH™
Clear-Mind Buddhism
Transcendental Awareness Institute
1-6055 Kettle River FSR East
Westbridge, BC V0H 1Y0

CANADA